african cichlids of lakes malawi and tanganyika

Lamprologus leleupi. Photo by H.J. Richter.

by dr. herbert r. axelrod
and dr. warren e. burgess

**Eighth Edition,
Revised**

Cover: *Trematocranus jacobfreibergi.* Photo by H. J. Richter.

Photos in this book, unless otherwise credited, are by Dr. Herbert R. Axelrod.

ISBN 0-87666-515-6

Distributed in the U.S.A. by T.F.H. Publications, Inc., 211 West Sylvania Avenue, P.O. Box 27, Neptune City, N.J. 07753; in England by T.F.H. (Gt. Britain) Ltd., 13 Nutley Lane, Reigate, Surrey; in Canada to the book store and library trade by Clarke, Irwin & Company, Clarwin House, 791 St. Clair Avenue West, Toronto 10, Ontario; in Canada to the pet trade by Rolf C. Hagen Ltd., 3225 Sartelon Street, Montreal 382, Quebec; in Southeast Asia by Y.W. Ong, 9 Lorong 36 Geylang, Singapore 14; in Australia and the south Pacific by Pet Imports Pty. Ltd., P.O. Box 149, Brookvale 2100, N.S.W., Australia. Published by T.F.H. Publications, Inc. Ltd., The British Crown Colony of Hong Kong.

Printed in the U.S.A.

TABLE OF CONTENTS

Back Row: Warren E. Burgess, Dr. Herbert R. Axelrod, Glen Axelrod. *Front Row:* Henny and Peter Davies. Photo by Evelyn Axelrod.

DEDICATION

This book is dedicated to Peter and Henny Davies of Cape McClear, Lake Malawi for all the beautiful fishes they found and made available for aquarists.

The great lakes of East Africa, with the major associated river systems, and barriers—waterfalls and rapids—which have been and are important in the isolation of various basins.

Introduction

It was not more than 100 years ago that the first Europeans discovered the great lakes of Africa, but since that time there have been numerous expeditions and quantities of scientific studies dealing with Lakes Victoria, Nyasa (Malawi) and Tanganyika. Foremost of the scientists writing about these lakes are Dr. Ethelwynn Trewavas of the British Museum and her associate Dr. P. H. Greenwood, Dr. Geoffrey Fryer, and Dr. Max Poll.

The fishes of Lakes Malawi and Tanganyika are of special interest to aquarists because there are hundreds of interesting cichlids which are found only in these lakes; many of these cichlids are richly colored and have interesting feeding and breeding habits.

Both of these lakes are being exploited for their aquarium fishes by active, dependable collectors who have long experience in fish collecting and who practice sound principles of conservation. Specifically, Pierre Brichard, working out of Bujumbura, Burundi, sends out about 100 boxes (about 5000 fishes) per week of mostly Tanganyikan cichlids; in Malawi Peter Davies, along with his wife Henny, ships about the same quantity of mainly Malawian cichlids. It is to these two gentlemen that the aquarium world owes a great deal of thanks, for without their perseverance and dedication, few fishes, if any, would ever grace our tanks.

The sketch and caption were taken from Fryer and Iles' "The Cichlid Fishes of the Great Lakes of Africa."

Aerial view of Lake Malawi about 10 miles from Monkey Bay at a height of 800 feet.

Lake Malawi has islands which remind the author of oceanic coral islands, and peninsulas such as this one, which provide habitats for the many cichlids found there.

1

The Lakes

Lakes Tanganyika and Malawi are large lakes, being the seventh and ninth largest lakes in the world. Tanganyika has an area of 34,000 square kilometres (13,124 square miles), while Malawi has an area of about 30,000 square kilometers (11,430 square miles). Lake Malawi reaches a depth of about 750 metres, almost half a mile, while Lake Tanganyika is almost 1500 meters deep, or almost a mile. The acidity, or rather alkalinity, of the lakes' waters varies. Lake Malawi's pH value fluctuates between 7.7 and 8.6, while Tanganyika is much more alkaline, with its pH varying between 8.6 and 9.2. This is important information for the aquarist, since the fish do not do well in neutral or acid water.

Not all Malawian shores are rocky. Certain areas, shown in the photos above and below, are sandy. Unfortunately the colorful fishes are found among the rocks, where they are much more difficult to capture.

Huge rocks under the water support a ½-inch thick crust of algae which are grazed upon by cichlid fishes. This scene is in 12 feet of water near Cape McClear.

What is so unbelievable is that Lake Malawi has more different species of fishes than any other lake anywhere in the world, while Lake Tanganyika is third in this respect. Lake Victoria, by the way, also one of Africa's great lakes, ranks second.

I do not think of these bodies of water as lakes, because they are so unlike the lakes I know in South America. I prefer to think of these lakes as oceans, because they, like the oceans, contain many islands and almost every island has its own special fauna of cichlid fishes. Surely many of the islands have the same fishes, but more often than not the fishes, although very similar in body form, have different color patterns, and it is quite questionable whether they are truly the same species or whether they are sub-species . . . they might even be distinct species. More scientific work is clearly indicated.

A view of Monkey Bay, Lake Malawi (above), taken from a hill overlooking the bay. Photo by David Eccles. Below is Lake Tanganyika photographed from the Bujumbura, Burundi shore with the Congo (Zaire) Mountains in the background.

Muddy water runs through Tanganyika and Uganda, bringing nutrient salts in the silt to Lake Victoria. Aerial view at 3,000 feet.

Swamplands and marshes also can be found in Lake Malawi. The photo above was taken at 2,000 feet and shows Lake Malawi near Monkey Bay. The lower photo is a closeup of the marshland.

Lake Malawi has muddy bank ecological niches as well. The high grass also grows underwater and for all purposes this scene might just as well be underwater.

At latest count, Lake Malawi probably has 250 species of cichlids; if they were to be broken down further into "subspecies" or color varieties, the total might reach 375. Lake Tanganyika has about 150 species of cichlids. What is especially interesting is that of the 250 species of cichlids found in Lake Malawi, fewer than half a dozen are found anywhere else in the world. As a matter of fact, the Malawian cichlids are not even found in the rivers which flow into Lake Malawi. Lake Tanganyika is even more isolated. Of the 150 species of cichlids known from that lake, NONE ARE FOUND ANYWHERE ELSE! Scientists call a species "endemic" when it is found in only one lake or river; thus every Tanganyikan cichlid is endemic to Lake Tanganyika. One species, *Tilapia rendalli,* is the only Malawian cichlid which even comes close to Tanganyika Lake. It is not found in the lake itself, however, only in certain rivers which flow into the lake. Thus aquarists have a lot of cichlids to look forward to seeing in the near future.

Outside Mombasa, Kenya,
a few hundred feet into the
Indian Ocean, islands are
found which are quite similar
to those found in Lake Malawi.

Pierre Brichard searching for Tanganyikan cichlids in about 30 feet of water. Brichard uses an anaesthesia (quinaldine dissolved in acetone) to stun the fish as they hide in the tiny crevices between the rocks.

In 1972 and 1973 I made several expeditions to both lakes, being unable to explore Lake Victoria because of the unfriendly attitude of President Amin of Uganda, who controls Lake Victoria. But I was able to dive in both Lake Malawi and Lake Tanganyika. I can highly recommend diving in those lakes, for their waters are clear and clean and free of the horrible parasite *Schistosoma*, which the Africans call *"Bilharzia,"* an obsolete scientific name. *Schistosoma*, a fluke, is carried by snails.

Diving is relatively safe in these lakes, though the hippos and crocodiles may present a problem at times. I had a close call with a huge electric catfish in Tanganyika, and my diving partner, Thierry Brichard, was almost bitten by a diving cobra which coiled ready to strike . . . underwater!

Lake Malawi, according to Fryer and Iles' magnificent book *The Cichlid Fishes of the Great Lakes of Africa,* contains more than 200 species of cichlids, of which all except 4 are endemic. It has about 42 other species of fishes, of which about 26 are endemic.

The tide is seasonal in Lake Malawi, with the lake falling during the dry season and rising during the rainy season. The rings around the rocks give some idea of the tide. Since algae grows only to a fairly low water depth, after which there is not enough light to support plant growth, the low tide season enables algae to grow in areas where it would not normally survive.

During the rainy season water flows out of Lake Tanganyika and Lake Malawi since they are very high in the mountains. Dirty silt-laden water enters the lakes and clean water leaves.

According to Fryer and Iles, Lake Tanganyika has 126 species of cichlids, all endemic, and 67 other fishes of which 47 are endemic. These estimates are conservative as many new species have been discovered since their work was published.

The cichlids of these lakes vary in size from the tiny *Lamprologus kungweensis* of Lake Tanganyika, which measures only 1½ inches in length, to the comparatively enormous *Boulengerochromis microlepis,* which measures about 2½ feet in length. The largest cichlid weighs 800 times more than the smallest!

Since the lakes are fairly deep you would expect cichlids to be found at most depths, but most of the fishes are found in the top 50 feet. The cichlids living at the lower portion of the 50-foot depth range present severe problems in collecting, because fishes found in 50 feet of water or deeper have to be decompressed before they can be safely maintained in aquaria. Cichlids, like most other bony fishes, have a gas-filled swim bladder which must be adjusted slowly to varying depths. Thus a cichlid living at a depth of 50 feet might explode if brought up to the surface

The rock in the foreground is white from bird droppings. This is a typical habitat of mbuna cichlids in Lake Malawi.

Pierre Brichard with his "decompression chamber" for fishes. Brichard found it necessary to decompress all his fishes which were captured at a depth of about 20 feet or more.

too quickly, and in many of our seine hauls we found that in cichlids caught at 50 to 100 feet of depth the swim bladder would be so distended that it pushed the intestines out of the anus. Brichard invented a decompression chamber which was a barrel of about 50-gallon capacity which had a relief valve for the pressure to be slowly adjusted. Cichlids brought up from 25 feet also had swim bladder problems; their buoyancy when brought up swiftly resulted in their struggling belly-up for hours before they could relieve the air pressure in their bladders. One disadvantage of cichlid swim bladders (which are called "physoclistous" swim bladders) is that they have no direct connection to the outside of the fish, and air is secreted and absorbed slowly. Cichlid fishes have been found as deep as 215 meters in Lake Tanganyika.

Can you believe this scene? It is in only 16 feet of water in Lake Tanganyika. The fish in the foreground are *Lamprologus brichardi*; the single fish is *Julidochromis marlieri*.

The four Malawian fishes on this and the facing page were all taken from water over 25 feet deep. They were brought to the surface too quickly and their extended swim bladder is forcing their intestines out of their bodies.

Page 24, top: *Lethrinops gossei* ; page 24, bottom: *Haplochromis hennydaviesae*; p.25, top: *Haplochromis sphaerodon;* page 25, bottom: *Haplochromis annectens.*

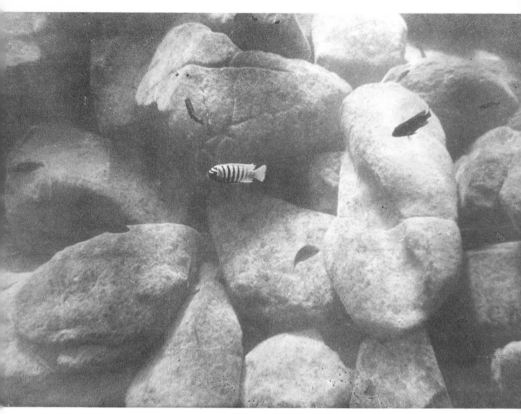

This is a typical habitat of mbuna cichlids in Lake Malawi.

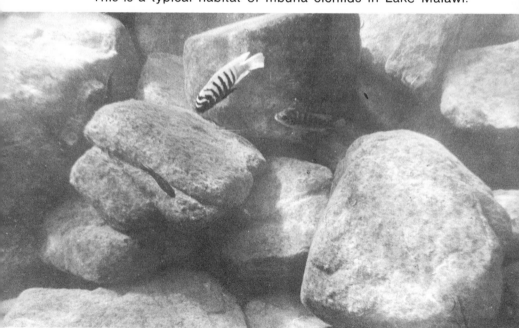

2

Peculiarities of Certain African Cichlids

There is something special about certain cichlids. Many fishes which have physoclistous (sealed) air bladders, develop the "seal" only after they, in their fry stage, have taken a gulp of air to initially fill their bladder with air. Once the bladder is filled, the duct seals itself and the fish no longer requires a visit to the surface. Some cichlids have so progressed that they no longer must take that first gulp of air. This is important because we know that African cichlids always spawn close to the bottom of an aquarium; in the African lakes they are never found spawning near the surface but always on the bottom. They watch and protect their young closely, and if the young had to escape to the surface to catch an air bubble, the parental behavior pattern would be broken. Cichlid fishes exhibit, almost universally, a range of parental care from simple guarding of the eggs and fry to orally incubating the eggs and utilizing their buccal cavity for a safe retreat for their free-swimming offspring.

The spines of fishes have long been utilized by ichthyologists to help identify fishes. Cichlids from all over the world have from 2 to 12 spines in their anal fins, but African cichlids all have 6 anal spines or fewer . . . except for certain cichlids found in Lake Tanganyika. Also, except for one species, the cichlids of Lakes Victoria and Malawi have only 3 anal spines.

Most of the cichlid species of these lakes have interesting teeth which have evolved to become specially suited to certain feeding habits. These feeding habits change as the fishes grow. Certainly adult fishes which prefer other fishes' eyeballs, or which scrape the scales from the tails of even larger species, would hardly be

27

Compare the shape of the head, mouth and lips of this fish, *Diplotaxodon ecclesi*, with *Lethrinops gossei* on the facing page.

(a) shows a side view of the Malawian eye-eater,

Haplochromis compressiceps; (b) is a closeup of the mouth.
Photos from Fryer and Iles *"The Cichlid Fishes of the Great
Lakes of Africa."*

able to have the same diet when they are young and very small. Thus the teeth of a fish are very important only when fishes of the same age and/or size are compared. Many ichthyologists failed to take into account this change in dentition when they described small fishes as being different species.

The mouths of our African cichlids are used for other things besides eating. Like most other teleost fishes, African cichlids "inhale" water through their mouths and squirt it over their 4 pairs of gills in the familiar chewing motion. The gills exchange oxygen for carbon dioxide the same way (more or less) that our own lungs operate. Humans and other mammals do not have to open their mouths to breathe . . . cichlids do. But cichlids also use their mouths, in many cases, for brooding fry and eggs, so this same breathing apparatus enables the developing eggs and fry to be aerated with fresh water automatically as their parent "breathes." Cichlids do, by the way, have nostrils, but these nostrils end in dead-end sacs, and their function is in no way directly connected with breathing.

Like many other fishes, African cichlids show different coloration between adult males and females in many cases. They also have color patterns which manifest themselves during periods of fright or breeding or brooding, and they have nighttime colors and juvenile colors. Probably the juvenile coloration is for camouflage purposes as well as for recognition, because almost certainly the colors of the juveniles are less accentuated than those of a breeding male.

Besides basic overall color, there are certain color patterns in the fins of the fishes. The so called "egg spots" of some of the cichlids has been well publicized by Dr. Wickler, who wrote extensively to show that the egg spots found on the anal fins of the males of mouth brooding species assisted the female of the species to fertilize the eggs in her mouth. Wickler proposed that the female would peck at the egg spots, perhaps thereby stimulating the male to release sperm, thus enabling the female to get a mouthful of sperm with which to fertilize the eggs in her buccal cavity. *I disagree with Wickler.* I propose that the eggs spots are used solely for identification. Cichlids in many cases spawn and court in relatively secret quarters. We know that in the aquarium they prefer dark caves and dig under rocks and logs to spawn as secretly as possible. While diving under huge boulders in Lakes Malawi and Tanganyika, all I could see sometimes were the spots on the anal fins of the males. It was probably too dark for the

31

In support of his theory on egg spots, Dr. Wickler published the drawing above. The drawing seems to have been made from the photo below by Rudolf Zukal. The scene depicts a female picking up eggs as the male fertilizes them. A close view will indicate the female is not "attacking" the spots at all.

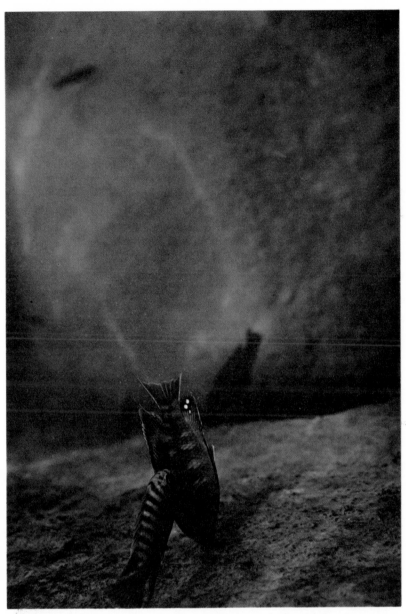

In the darkness under huge boulders in Lake Malawi every-
thing is green and murky. . .except for the glowing identification marks on the anal fins of some mbunas.

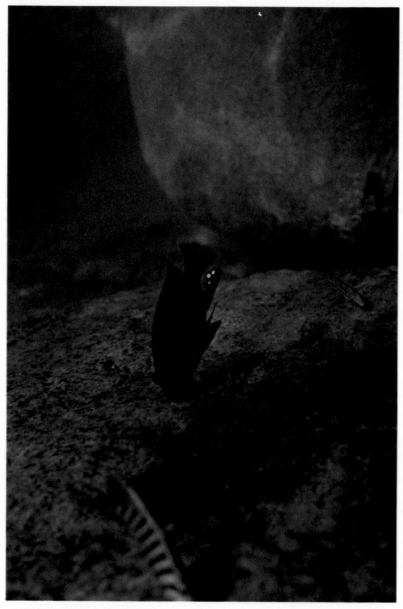

The photograph above and those on the facing page show
how well the egg spots show up on fishes in the deep and
poorly lit areas under the boulders some 20-30 feet deep in
Lake Malawi. The author contends these spots are for identification and are not to trick the female into trying to snatch
the "eggs" from the male's anal fin.

male to make out prospective mating partners, so they waited for females to come their way. A female probably signals her acceptance by pecking at the male's anal fin spots, thus making it easier for the fish to find each other both initially and during the spawning process. Thus I reject completely the "egg spot" theory of Wickler in favor of my own "color recognition" theory. Fortunately I was able to take some photographs underwater in Lake Malawi to demonstrate my observations.

Cichlids, by the way, can change their colors quickly. I have often caught a brilliantly colored breeding male only to have him fade away after a few moments to a common-looking fish even before I could put him into a photo tank.

Still further proof exists for the rejection of the egg spot theory. There are many color varieties or "morphs" of certain species. Some are striped, some have solid colors, and some are yellow, while their morphs are blue or banded. Those fishes which have

Haplochromis placodon. The female, above, and the male in the lower photograph, show very clearly that this fish has egg spots in every unpaired fin except the anal!! A closeup of the dorsal and caudal fins on the facing page shows typical egg spots which would be unexplainable by the egg spot theory of Dr. Wickler.

Haplochromis sphaerodon is another fish which has egg spots in its dorsal and caudal fins and none in its anal fin. The upper photo is a closeup of the unpaired fins.

Haplochromis taeniolatus, above, has no egg spots at all, while *Hemitilapia oxyrhynchus* has egg spots in the dorsal and caudal but none in the anal fin. All of this evidence has convinced the author that the Wickler egg spot theory must be rejected.

Haplochromis polystigma in breeding dress (above) and in its usual color pattern (below). It is interesting that the egg spots on the anal fin are only visible when the fish is *not* in breeding color.

Haplochromis similis has almost perfect egg spots in its dorsal fin only.

dark morphs always seem to have bright egg spots, while those brighter colored morphs have, at times, no egg spots at all! The brighter fish are never found under rocks but almost always are found alongside or atop rocks . . . the darker fish never spawn in the open.

Further evidence in support of the recognition theory is the behavior manifest when a male sees a ripe female. Almost immediately, the male will spread his fins, fully extending his anal and dorsal fins as well, and begin to "dance" in front of the female, showing as clearly as possible the egg spots and other recognition signs on his fins and body. In many species of African cichlids the unpaired fins (anal, dorsal and caudal) are significantly marked and show more variation between species in many closely related fishes than do meristic (measurable) characteristics.

There are at least four described morphs of *Pseudotropheus zebra*. In the BB morph of Fryer and Iles both sexes have alternating blue and black vertical bars shown in the fish above.

In the B morph the fish are from a sky blue to a mauve in color, sexes being colored alike. This fish, by the way, was photographed in the aquarium in the lobby of the Monkey Bay Hotel of Mr. and Mrs. Otto.

These photos are of one of the original specimens of *Labido-chromis fryeri*. The fish apparently came from Mumbo Island, Lake Malawi and was exhibited in an aquarium in the lobby at the Monkey Bay Hotel.

In the OB morph the fish are orange blotched, a color pattern which is more common for females than for males.

In nature some color patterns seem to overlap and to deter-
mine which zebra morph they are is difficult.

Whilst diving in 25 feet of water near Cape McClear, I spotted this *Pseudotropheus* which seems to be a reverse *tropheops* pattern. There were about a dozen fish with this coloration in the area which I visited. Below is a normal *Pseudotropheus tropheops* male.

These two fish are also known as *Pseudotropheus tropheops* sensu Jackson. It is doubtful that they are identical to the fish on the opposite page of the same name even though their meristic characters overlap. When sufficient specimens are available for study it is almost certain these fish will be considered a subspecies or separate species.

These two fish (female holotype above, male paratype below) were discovered in Lake Malawi by Peter and Henny Davies and described as a new species, *Pseudotropheus johanni*, by Eccles. The name was recently changed to *Melanochromis johanni*.

A closeup of the head of the holotype of the recently described *Melanochromis simulans*.

A closeup of the head of the holotype of *Melanochromis johanni*.

The fish above is the recently described *Melanochromis simulans*, so called because of its striking similarity to *Melanochromis auratus* shown below.

I chased this fish into 40 feet of water to take its photograph. It is a morph of *Pseudotropheus tropheops*, but I cannot exactly say which one. Note the poor condition of this fish. Below is a *Labeotropheus trewavasae* which might have had an encounter with a scale eater that chopped off a piece of its caudal fin.

These two fishes are in the "utaka" group taken in fairly deep water by trawl. They belong to the genus *Haplochromis* but I was unable to get a species-positive identification.

3
Rocks and Islands

The aerial views of Lake Malawi show to some degree why it and the other large African lakes remind me of the oceans. The more rocks found in a particular area, the more fishes . . . especially more cichlids, even though not all cichlids by any means are found exclusively around rocks. Many species are found in open water, but in most cases these open water forms cannot be readily caught because of their swim bladder problems when seined from any appreciable depth and because in most cases the deep water forms are not highly colored.

A typical scene in twenty feet of water in Lake Malawi. The number of fishes is staggering . . . but catching them is another story.

The scenes above and below are at 25 feet depth near Cape McClear, Lake Malawi. The rocks are covered with a thin layer of algae which are constantly being grazed upon by various fishes. Note the angle at which the fishes attack the algae and pay attention to the many dark "holes" in which the fishes hide and spawn.

Cyphotilapia frontosa in their typical habitat in Lake Tanganyika.

The cichlids of Lake Malawi found around the rocks have been called *"mbuna"* after the native name used near Nkata Bay. Other areas of Lake Malawi refer to the rock-inhabiting fishes under different names. "Mbuna" is pronounced "mmmmmboona" and not "em-boona" as I have previously written. "Em-boona" is the way a European would pronounce it, being unaccustomed to swallowing the "m" the way Africans do without parting their lips to enunciate the "m."

The basic habitat of the shore fishes of Lakes Malawi and Tanganyika are rocks, grassy or sandy open areas between the rocks and the grass. The accompanying photographs show very well the differences between these habitats, and it is exceedingly rare that mbunas stray from their particular ecological niche. Since the rocky areas, especially the islands, are more or less isolated within the lake, in order for an mbuna to get from one area to another he would have to cross open water. Mbunas refuse to cross open waters.

All of the rocky habitat fishes in both Tanganyika and Malawi insist upon keeping their belly region pointed to the rocks, so

The photographs above and below are taken in 8 feet (lower photo) and 20 feet (upper photo) of water in the sandy, grassy habitats to be found in Lake Malawi. Note the protective coloration of the fishes.

A closer view of the Lake Malawi sandy, grassy habitat which more clearly shows the kinds of fishes found in this habitat. Below is a sandy area in Lake Tanganyika which shows *Cyathopharynx furcifer* circling over their huge nest. The fish in the foreground is *Cyphotilapia frontosa.*

The photographs on these two facing pages should be evaluated for protective coloration. The *Pseudotropheus zebra* BB morph shown in the two top photos shows this color form venturing from their normal rocky habitat. In the intermediate area between rocks and grass where there is just sand, spotted or striped fishes seem to be more at ease. The golden barb in the lower right hand photograph is perfectly colored. Note the huge deposit of fish excretion on the bottom. This disintegrates into a fine mulm amongst which the barbs like to poke.

when they swim above the rocks they swim in a normal position. When they swim alongside the rocks they swim with their bellies parallel to the rocky surface and when they are underneath the rocks they swim upside down. Is it any wonder that most mbunas and even *Pelvicachromis* spawn upside down inside flowerpots? This probably derives from their habit of spawning in dark caves underneath a rock. More evidence for my anti-egg spot theory.

On these facing pages are four different color varieties of *Pseudotropheus zebra* though all would be placed into the BB morph. BB, by the way, stands for "black bar." The W morph indicates "white"; the B morph are "blue" and the OB morph is "orange blotched".

Note on these facing pages that the lighter the fish the lighter the habitat in which it is found. Note how well the egg spots stand out in the darker areas.

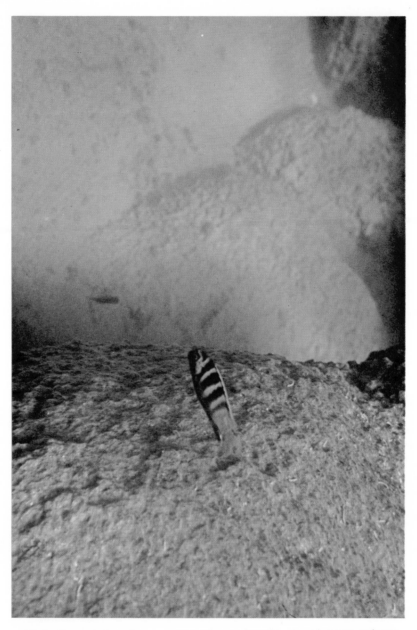

This *Pseudotropheus microstoma* (or *Ps. tropheops micro-stoma* as some people would have it) had more black than any of the "zebra-striped" morphs I ever saw. This specimen was in some 35 feet of water. Note all the fish excreta on the rock.

Labeotropheus trewavasae, above; below, *Haplochromis tetrastigma*, which is found in shallow water where it finds the bottom epiphytes upon which it feeds.

These two photos, above and below, were taken within a few feet of each other and show the typical assortment of fishes found on the rocks (mbuna) and those which venture out onto the sand. Malawian fishes have a definite preference for habitats and fish collectors know in advance what species of fishes can be found in any particular habitat.

4
How Cichlids feed

Cichlids have been successful in the African lakes because they have found ways to feed on practically every living resource in their range. They have developed specialized teeth and mouth structures, and they even have developed specialized internal organs with which to utilize special foods.

Many *Tilapia*, for example, feed on microscopic plants and animalcules which are collectively referred to as phytoplankton. Herring and menhaden are similar feeders, and like certain *Tilapia* (but by no means ALL *Tilapia*) they cannot be caught

Fishes such as *Labeotropheus* with mouths located on the underside of their bodies feed upon the algae in an almost horizontal position to the strata upon which they are feeding.

In 12 feet of water where the rocky meets the grassy, sandy habitat the fishes enjoy ample food supplies. Different genera feed at different angles due to the formation of their mouths and jaws.

This photo was taken in 4 feet of water where the *aufwuchs* is very thick due to the increased amount of light falling upon the surface of the rocks.

on hook and line. Basically, phytoplanktonic feeders merely suck in food on a continuous basis, filtering out those particles which are edible and ingesting them. They have special gill filaments which assist in the filtering process. In captivity it is possible to feed these fishes the usual aquarium fare, for many of them also have teeth.

Many phytoplankton feeders also feed from the bottom on sediment, thus emphasizing the fact that their teeth might have some ancillary use. I was quite amazed at the numbers of *Tilapia* which followed the hippos, awaiting their bowel movements to rush at the droppings in a frenzy. Mbunas rarely peck at bottom sediment, and it was quite interesting to note the huge amount of droppings accumulated on the flat stones and sandy bottoms near the mbuna sites. So thick was the sediment near mbuna sites that the water was stirred to a muddy cloud by the action of my flippers when I swam by. This was extremely annoying, as it made picture-taking very difficult; I had to remove my flippers to take successful photographs in such areas.

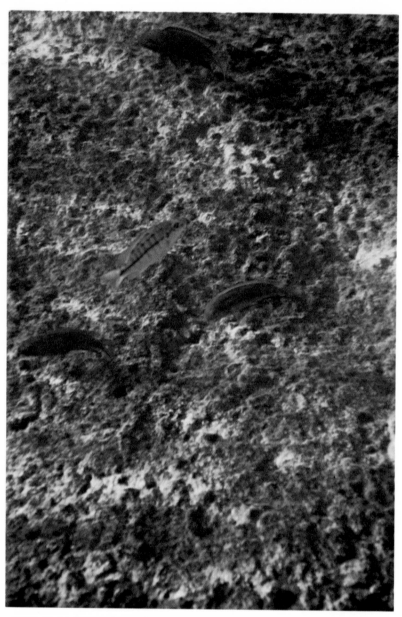

This is a smooth rock which has been covered with *auf-wuchs*, the algae upon which the entire mbuna population is dependent for food.

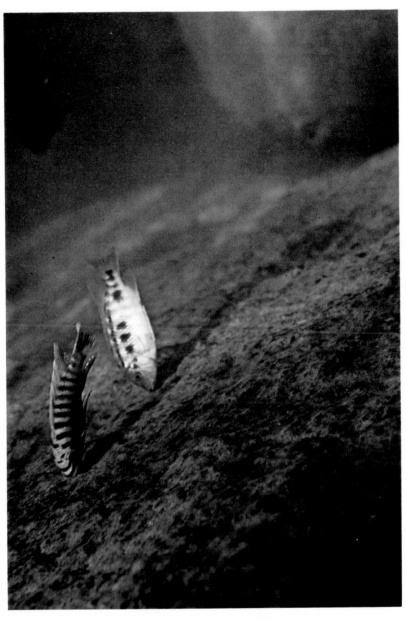

This photograph clearly shows the different angles that fishes use to attack the *aufwuchs* (algae). This photo was taken in 12 feet of water near Cape McClear, Lake Malawi.

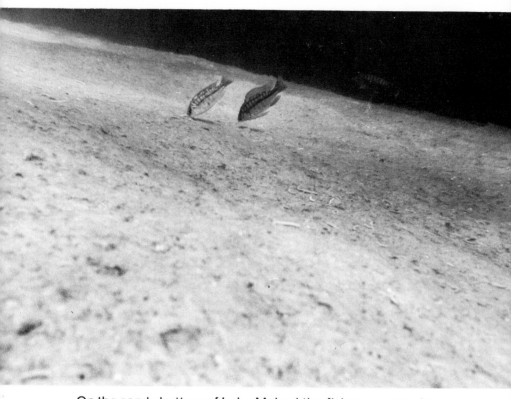

On the sandy bottom of Lake Malawi the fishes seem to have a 45° angle of attack. They grab mouthfuls of sand, sift it through their gills, and remove those bits of nutrition which are available.

The mbunas are what the Germans call *aufwuchs* feeders. The name *aufwuchs*, which literally means "luxuriant growth", is applied to the half-inch thick covering of slimy algae which covers the rocks' surfaces in which the mbunas are found. *Pseudotropheus tropheops* and all its many morphs are found feeding solely on such algal growth; the fish's 8 rows of small teeth assist it to scrape off mouthfuls of this high protein food. In the aquarium they usually adapt to eating almost anything, partly accounting for their success as an aquarium fish, but if you really want to see them at work, put in a piece of lettuce or spinach and watch them go to work reducing it to a few fine strands. *P. zebra* and *P. fuscus*, even though they have quite different dentition, also feed on this same aufwuchs, as do the *Tropheus* of Lake Tanganyika.

The *aufwuchs* found on the Lake Malawi rocks (upper photo) is quite different from that found in Lake Tanganyika (below). Note the sponges (green in natural color) in the Tanganyikan habitat.

Petrotilapia tridentiger from Lake Malawi.

Petrochromis fasciolatus from Lake Tanganyika.

Tilapia rendalli from Lake Tanganyika.

Lethrinops furcicauda from Lake Malaw

Heads, jaws and teeth of a scraper of rocks and leaves, and a rock-scraper, from L. Malawi. 65–68—*Cyathochromis obliquidens*: 65—Head, lateral; 66—Head, anterior; 67—Upper dentition; 68—Opposing outer teeth of upper and lower jaws. 69–72—*Petrotilapia tridentiger*: 69—Head, lateral; 70—Head, dorsal; 71—Single tooth seen from the side, with detail of its expanded tip in face view; 72—Head, anterior

The sketches and caption above were taken from Fryer and Iles' *"The Cichlid Fishes of the Great Lakes of Africa."*

One Malawian cichlid, *Petrotilapia tridentiger,* has spoon-shaped teeth and a flexible mouth that fits to the irregular shape of the rock surface, enabling the fish to very efficiently remove the aufwuchs. In the Chitonga language of Malawi, these fish are called *"mbuna kumwa,"* which means "rock hitter," referring to the way these fish "attack" a rock. The *Petrochromis* species from Tanganyika are remarkably similar in habit. It is fairly easy, by the way, to identify certain genera of cichlids from a distance just by watching their feeding habits. *Petrotilapia* and *Petro-*

Heads, jaws and teeth of an algal-eating rock scraper, a specialist picker of algal filaments, and a general *Aufwuchs* eater all from L. Malawi; 73–77—*Labeotropheus fuelleborni*: 73—Head, lateral; 74—Heads, ventral; 75—Jaws, semi-ventral, with mouth open; 76—Anterior row of teeth, anterior; 77—Single tooth from this row, lateral. 78–79—*Haplochromis guentheri*: 78—Head, lateral; 79—Upper dentition. 80–82—*H. fenestratus*: 80—Head, lateral; 81—Head, anterior; 82—Upper dentition

The sketches and caption above were taken from Fryer and Iles' *"The Cichlid Fishes of the Great Lakes of Africa."*

chromis usually attack a rocky surface perpendicular to it. *Pseudotropheus* species are found at a 45° angle when feeding, while *Labeotropheus* species are almost parallel to the rocky surface when they feed, facilitated of course by their ventral mouths.

Amongst the algal growths are to be found many small copepods, but since the fish usually scrape away the algae and "inhale" what they scraped away while preparing for the next scrape, they give the free-swimming copepods a chance to swim away from the mild stream flowing into the fish's mouth, so a careful observation

Head study of *Haplochromis mloto.*

Head study of *Haplochromis placodon.*

Heads, jaws and teeth of three algal-eating rock scrapers from
L. Malawi. 54–57—*Pseudotropheus tropheops*: 54—Head, lateral; 55—Dentition
of upper jaw; 56—Details of bicuspid and tricuspid teeth of upper jaw; 57—
Head, anterior. 58–60—*P. zebra*; 58—Head, lateral; 59—Head, anterior; 60—
Arrangement of tricuspid teeth of posterior rows. 61–64—*P. fuscus*: 61—Head,
lateral; 62—Head anterior; 63—Arrangement of teeth in upper jaw; 64—Teeth
of outer row of upper jaw

The sketches and caption above were taken from Fryer and
Iles' *"The Cichlid Fishes of the Great Lakes of Africa."*

of the fish feeding shows only a scattering of small copepods. In
the aquarium all the known species (known to aquarists, that is)
readily adapt to feeding on the usual aquarium diet. They do
especially well on prepared foods and while living foods are
accepted, they do not seem to suffer from a lack of living foods
the way South American cichlids do.

Heads, jaws and teeth of a plant scraper and a leaf chopper from
L. Malawi. 83–85—*Hemitilapia oxyrhynchus*: 83—Head, lateral; 84—Head,
anterior; 85—Upper dentition. 86–88—*Haplochromis similis*: 86—Head, lateral;
87—Part of upper dentition; 88—Outer teeth of upper jaw, lateral

Some cichlids, notably *Haplochromis similis*, *Tilapia rendalli*
and *T. zillii*, prefer leafy plants. While their diet presumably
depends upon water plants, they graze on any leaf, and the
African fishermen take advantage of this fact. Several fishermen I
observed dumped sweet potatoes, yams and casava leaves into an
easily seined area and left the deposit there for a few hours before
they seined the area to catch the fishes which were feeding upon
the leaves. I examined the stomach contents of several of these
fishes and found them filled with these heavy leaves.

Some of the larger species of cichlids, such as *Chilotilapia* of
Lake Malawi, *Macropleurodus* of Lake Victoria, and *Haplochromis
sauvagei*, eat snails and mussels. Some of these fishes merely
crush the snails, many of which are two inches in diameter,
while others merely grasp the extended foot and shake the body
out of the shell.

The usual feeding habits of many fishes depend upon eating
other fishes or aquatic and terrestrial insects and crustaceans.
Lethrinops furcifer from Lake Malawi, for example, is found only
on sandy stretches near the shore, and its sole diet seems to be
small worm-like larvae found in the sand. The fish merely dives
headfirst into the sand, gathering a mouthful of sand which it
passes through its gill rakers, filtering out the small larvae. A fish

Many Malawian cichlids dig into the sand, scoop up a mouthful and pass it over the gill raker sieves to remove food particles. The sketches show successive positions of *Lethrinops furcifer* and two types of gill rakers The shape of the gill rakers is very important in the classification of fishes. The photograph was taken by H. Hansen in the Berlin Aquarium. The sketches are from Fryer and Iles' *"The Cichlid Fishes of the Great Lakes of Africa."*

This fish was caught in fairly deep water. It represents a new genus and species, *Cleithrochromis bowleyi* from Lake Malawi; it was recently described by Mr. Eccles. The "Mae West" appearance might well serve to protect the fish from digging too deeply into the bottom (see sketch on facing page).

Diggers in sand from L. Malawi. 97–99—Successive positions as *Lethrinops furcifer* fills its mouth with sand and passes collected material through its gill raker sieve; 100—Outermost row of gill rakers; 101—Outermost row of gill rakers. *Lethrinops* sp. (Note the difference in spacing of the gill rakers, which is associated with selection of different foods by these closely related species.)

A zooplankton feeder and two scale eaters from L. Malawi.
121–124—*Cynotilapia afra*: 121—Head, lateral; 122—Teeth of upper jaw; 123
—Head, dorsal; 124—Head, anterior. 125–129—*Genyochromis mento*: 125—
Head, lateral; 126—Head, dorsal; 127—Head, anterior; 128—Outer tooth of
lower jaw; 129—Inner tooth of lower jaw. 130–131—*Corematodus shiranus*:
130—Head, lateral; 131—Upper dentition.

The sketches and caption above were taken from Fryer and
Iles' *"The Cichlid Fishes of the Great Lakes of Africa."*

I collected in open waters with a seine, a new genus and species
probably, has a sort of shield on its chest which might very well
protect it from being buried in the sand when it may be diving
for such mouthfuls of sand. This is merely speculation on my
part, as I did not observe the fish feeding. *Lethrinops* would
probably do best in the aquarium when fed *Tubifex* worms.

The scale eaters of L. Tanganyika and a fin biter from L. Malawi. 132 and 133—*Plecodus paradoxus*. 134—*Perissodus microlepis*. 135—*Plecodus straeleni*. 136—*Plecodus multidentatus*. 137—*Plecodus elaviae*. All show the jaws either laterally or from in front. 138 and 139—*Docimodus johnstoni*: 138—Head, lateral; 139—Dentition of the jaws. Redrawn after Boulenger and Poll.

The zooplankton feeders are fishes which feed upon the minute crustaceans living in the water. They all have protrusible jaws and have earned the name *"utaka,"* which seems to defy translation. They would do very well in the aquarium on a diet of *Daphnia* or brine shrimp, as crustaceans seem to be their preferred diet.

Haplochromis livingstonii, head study.

Haplochromis lepturus, head study.

Piscivores from L. Malawi. 140–142—*Haplochromis pardalis*: 140—Head, lateral; 141—Head, dorsal; 142—Head, anterior. 143–145—*H. Polyodon*: 143—Head, anterior; 144—Head, lateral; 145—Head, lateral, with mouth open.

The sketches and caption above were taken from Fryer and Iles' "The Cichlid Fishes of the Great Lakes of Africa."

In Lakes Tanganyika, Malawi and Victoria are to be found fishes which eat scales. Even South America has a piranha-like fish, *Catoprion mento*, which also is a scale eater. *Plecodus* and *Perissodus* species from Tanganyika eat scales, as does a *Haplochromis*, two species of *Corematodus* and *Genyochromis mento*. It is very interesting that almost all of these fishes have different dentition, indicating that their evolution was dissimilar.

Rocks and sand as they appear in Lake Malawi (upper photo) and Lake Tanganyika (lower photograph.)

Lethrinops gossei, female, head study.

Haplochromis mloto, head study.

Of the scale eaters, the *Corematodus* species are the fishes of most concern to aquarists, because they do not eat large scales like their homologous species, but prefer the small scales found on the tails of such small fishes as the mbunas. One of my first observations while diving among the mbuna was that they almost all had had chunks taken out of their tails.

In the aquarium the scale eaters seem to only eat scales! I do not know of any case where any scale eater, including *Catoprion mento*, lived for an extended period of time (say six months) unless it had fish scales in its diet! It is doubtful that the scale eaters restrict themselves to scales, as I have seen them remove fins (or at least parts of fins, especially the tail) in their attempts to remove scales.

In Lake Malawi there is a very interesting fish known as *Haplochromis compressiceps*. What makes this fish so special is that it attacks the eyes of fishes. I observed three *Haplochromis compressiceps* feeding and they attacked small fishes by aiming at their eyes and swallowing the whole fish. I saw two instances in which they attacked a fish almost twice their size and left an empty eye socket as a result of their attacks. They appear to

Catoprion mento is the South American scale-eater which resembles a piranha. The Germans call it the "Wimple Piranha" or the "Flag Piranha."

A closeup of the head and jaws of *Catoprion mento* from South America.

attack anything shining in the water, and hard-shelled insects were fed upon as well.

There are many other feeding specialists. Some rob eggs from nests, while some steal fry swimming about the nests. There are reports that certain fishes grasp brooding fishes by the mouth, forcing them to release their mouthful of eggs or fry into the mouth of the attacking fish. I have been unable to personally verify this feeding behavior.

To summarize, you should observe your African cichlids and attempt to ascertain their food of choice. It is rare (except for scale eaters) that a fish will eat only one food. In their range fishes probably specialize because they rarely leave the immediate neighborhood of their "home" and thus do not have the opportunity of a selective diet. Basically, mbunas are vegetarians while utakas prefer crustaceans, but I have seen mbunas rise to the surface of an aquarium as a flying insect hits the water, and I have also observed utakas eating a piece of lettuce.

Haplochromis pholidophorus, head study.

Haplochromis nitidus, head study.

5
How Cichlids Breed

The various kinds of mouths and teeth of African cichlids seem to have nothing to do with their breeding habits, even though African cichlids utilize their mouths in one way or another for breeding.

Those cichlids which lay their eggs on a flat, hard surface, usually use their mouths and teeth to scrub the surface clean before they lay their adhesive eggs. These eggs are then guarded and fanned until they hatch. Other species, and this pertains particularly to those species of cichlids found in Lakes Malawi and Tanganyika, are mouthbrooders. Especially in the Malawian endemic forms, the eggs, once laid and fertilized by the male, are gathered in the mouth of the mother fish and kept there until they hatch. Even after hatching, the young still flock to the mother's mouth for protection and safe harboring while they are growing.

Very few African fishes depend upon the father for buccal protection; the mother seems to be the one who cares the most! This characteristic is by no means peculiar to African cichlids. Many South American cichlids, a few anabantoids, and such truly ancient fishes as *Osteoglossum* (the aruana or arowana) also practice mouthbrooding.

Because of the physical problems involved in carrying first the eggs and then the young in their mouths, the size of the spawn of mouthbrooding cichlids is necessarily limited. Several scientists have counted the ripe eggs inside the body of dead fishes they collected. Often these eggs numbered thousands (a 10-inch *Tilapia aureum* had 4300 eggs; a 22-inch specimen of *Tilapia nilotica* had 3706), but never have this many eggs been found in any fish's mouth. In *Tilapia esculenta,* for example, as many as 1600 eggs have been found in ripened ovaries, but no one was ever able to find more than 711 eggs in any female's mouth.

The name *Tilapia mossambica* was recently changed to *Sarotherodon mossambicus* by Dr. E. Trewavas. It is a mouthbrooder in which both parents will care for the eggs and young, although it is almost always the females that take over the chores. The only species placed in the genus *Tilapia* are nest brooders; those in *Sarotherodon* are mouthbrooders.

Tilapia are quite different from mbuna. The *Tilapia* are, as a rule, hardier and more adaptable. They seem to thrive wherever they are introduced providing enough food is available and the water is sufficiently warm. For this reason we find *Tilapia* introduced into every continent in the world where rice is grown. Certainly, if you have *Tilapia*, you should be warned against releasing them into your local waters. It doesn't take too much for them to become established and crowd out native species. *Tilapia* are prohibited in many areas because of this problem.

Mbuna, on the other hand, would quickly perish without exactly perfect circumstances. They must have rocks and they must have soft, thick algae growing on those rocks. The brood size of most mbunas is probably well under 75 (Fryer claims that 50 eggs is probably the maximum), and often the ovaries of various mbuna contain but a few dozen ripened eggs. There is a record of 17 eggs in a ripe *Pseudotrópheus zebra* ovary; a *Labeotropheus trewavasae* had only 10 eggs in her mouth; *Tropehus moorii* carries between 5 and 10 eggs to incubate, while *Tropheus duboisi* laid a

Melanochromis auratus eggs three days old. Photo by Dr. D. Terver, Nancy Aquarium, Nancy, France.

Lethrinops sp., probably near *L. lethrinus.* Only a few species of *Lethrinops* are shipped from Lake Malawi. Photo by Aaron Norman.

Haplochromis incola from Lake Malawi. The position of the dark bands is useful in identifying some species of *Haplochromis.* Photo by Aaron Norman.

mere 10 eggs during an observed spawning. Is it any wonder tank-raised African mbunas are more expensive than the larger, wild-caught fishes?

Examinations of mbunas have produced evidence that only one ovary produces eggs, usually only the right ovary. Many *Haplochromis* have atrophied (smaller) right ovaries, especially in Lake Malawi, so it is possible that nature is protecting itself from overpopulation in Lake Malawi by limiting the number of eggs produced by cutting in half the number of ovaries producing eggs! That certainly could help the human overpopulation problem. Wouldn't it be nice if women produced eggs from only one ovary . . . every two months . . . cutting birthrates substantially?

The eggs of many African mouthbrooders are colorful. While most are eggyolk yellow, many have red in them, with the red changing the basic yellow color to orange, brown or tan. The eggs are fairly dense, usually with less than 60% water, and they are almost uniformly fairly large.

While diving in Lakes Malawi and Tanganyika, but especially in Lake Malawi, I was constantly amazed at the number and variety of nests to be observed in shallow water (under 30 feet deep) where there was sand. All of the nests were round and crater-like, but some were truncated cones and one was built on a huge, flat rock, the sand obviously having been carried from a distance by the male who was, at the time I observed the nest, guarding the site and moving off 10 to 20 feet at a time in all directions searching for a mate . . . or two.

I have observed at least five species spawning in Lake Malawi and several in Lake Tanganyika. Because I did not collect the fish it would be difficult to say exactly which species they were, but I will generalize about their spawning activities because they were all almost identical.

Using their nests as a base of operations, the males would swim inside large areas which seem to be bounded by an imaginary circle with a radius of ten feet from the center of the nest. They almost always moved in straight lines to the circumference of the circle to meet a fish who appeared to slowly approach the nest site. When the fish was of a different species . . . or another male of the same species . . . the nesting male would attack the fish sharply, driving it off. I never saw an intruding fish fight back: they always left the area quickly, even though they might have been larger than the nesting male. As the nesting male approached and noticed that the intruder was a female of the same species, he

A pair of *Sarotherodon mossambicus*. The male is the lower fish. In the photo below, a male *S. mossambicus* shows the lips characteristic of an older fish. Top photo by Milan Chvojka; lower photo by Gerhard Marcuse.

Pseudotropheus sp. (possibly *P. williamsi*). *Pseudotropheus williamsi*, the type species of the genus *Pseudotropheus*, has these characteristic dark spots on its back. Photo by Klaus Paysan.

The real *Pseudotropheus livingstonii*. This fish was often confused with the species now called *P. lanisticola*. Note the lack of the yellow bar on the anal fin. Photo by G. Meola, African Fish Imports.

Asprotilapia leptura is one of the sandy bottom species of Lake Tanganyika. It is a mouthbrooder according to P. Brichard. Photo by Pierre Brichard.

Grammatotria lemairei is also found on the sandy bottom habitats of Lake Tanganyika. It is reported to be a mouthbrooder holding up to 90 eggs. Photo by Pierre Brichard.

would immediately perform his ritual dance, spreading his fins to their fullest and showing clearly the markings in his tail, dorsal and anal fins. He would continue the dance for a minute or two, then swim back to his nest waiting for the female to follow. In most cases the female did not immediately follow the male, but would remain in the area just outside the imaginary boundary of the spawning area. The male, after waiting for a minute or two, would then swim back out to the female and try the same tactics all over again. This would be repeated, sometimes for hours, until finally the female came into the nesting arena, or she left.

Once the female arrives on the scene, the male invites her right onto his nest, and the female cautiously investigates. Her symbol of acceptance of the male seems to be her mouthing the nest herself. She then joins the male near the center of the nest. At this time the male seems to make passes on the center of the nest,

As the pair of *Sarotherodon mossambicus* prepare to spawn, they dig a deep hole in the sand.

As soon as the male fertilizes the eggs, the female takes them into her mouth. Note how this photograph compares in the position of the fishes with the egg-spot proof of Dr. Wickler on page 32 . . . and these males have no egg spots!

The male *Sarotherodon mossambicus.* Note the distended mouth pouch. Photo by Gerhard Marcuse.

The female *Julidochromis ornatus* joins the male and together they prepare the spawning site. Photo by H. J. Richter.

As the male waits, the female *Julidochromis ornatus* lays two eggs (not visible). Photo by H. J. Richter.

The male *J. ornatus* quickly fertilizes the pair of eggs laid by the female. Photo by H. J. Richter.

After spawning is completed the eggs are fanned and guarded by the female as they develop. Photo by H. J. Richter.

A male *Sarotherodon mossambicus* with fry. The fry are feeding on the microorganisms which are present on the algae-covered log. Photo by Gerhard Marcuse.

possibly laying down a stream of sperm. His action is almost exactly like those of male South American cichlids as they fertilize a chain of eggs previously laid by a female. After a short swim with his vent very close to the bottom of the nest, the male is joined by the female in a swim of increasingly tighter circles. Finally, in a circle so tight that the tail of one is almost in the mouth of the other, the pair snuggle next to one another and the eggs are laid amidst a substantial amount of quivering by both fish. All during the ceremony, the male proudly displays his anal fin eggspots; the female always seems to be impressed with them, even attacking them at times. Wickler suggests that during these attacks, she is able to get sperm to fertilize her mouthful of eggs, but probably it is merely a recognition sign which helps the fish distinguish one species from the other. Immediately after spawn-

The female *Sarotherodon mossambicus* signals her fry with a wriggle of her body, and they swiftly return to the refuge of her mouth. Photo by Gerhard Marcuse.

A young *Boulengerochromis microlepis.* This species grows very large, to 80 cm, and will probably not be offered very often to aquarists. Photo by Pierre Brichard.

An old but still impressive *Pseudotropheus zebra* BB. The hump on the head is a sign of older individuals. Photo by Klaus Paysan.

Two new imports from Lake Malawi which have not as yet been identified. They may turn out to be new species. Photos by Dr. Warren E. Burgess.

A male *Sarotherodon mossambicus* shows his distinctive white chin while guarding his free-swimming fry. The male of this species rarely takes part in the care of eggs or fry but may do so if they are neglected by the female. Photo by Gerhard Marcuse.

In *Tilapia macrochir,* the female mouths the genital tassel of the male. Her mouth is swollen with eggs. The thin string is a sperm thread and will facilitate fertilization of the eggs in the female's buccal cavity. Photo from Fryer and Iles' *"The Cichlid Fishes of the Great Lakes of Africa."*

ing, the female takes the eggs into her mouth and moves off the nesting site.

Typical of masculine behavior, once the female leaves the nesting site, the male immediately looks for another female. I saw one male spawn with three females within a 40-minute period. This same behavior might be observed in an aquarium, but it would have to be a fairly large one.

Another surprise characteristic of certain African cichlids is the elongated pelvic fins of *Ophthalmotilapia* and *Ophthalmochromis,* which are colored on the ends. Certain species of *Tilapia,* on the other hand, have special tassels hanging from the genital pore of the male and, during spawning, the female mouths them, assumedly getting confused between eggs and tassels and getting additional sperm in her mouth during the process.

When the female lays her eggs, they must be fertilized almost immediately, for a few moments later is too late. Though the time varies between species and water condition (pH, temperature,

Haplochromis compressiceps male starting to develop its breeding coloration. Photo by Ken Lucas, Steinhart Aquarium.

A recent import from Lake Malawi that has been going under the trade name of "chameleo." It has not been identified as yet. Photo by Aaron Norman.

A new morph of *Pseudotropheus zebra* called the "green zebra". Many more morphs are sure to be discovered in Lake Malawi and eventually imported to the United States. Photo by Aaron Norman.

Haplochromis quadrimaculatus is the name this species from Malawi is called in the hobby. Until specimens are obtained the identity cannot be confirmed. Photo by G. Meola, African Fish Imports.

As the thousand or so fry grow, they become more and more difficult to handle and they flee to both parents' mouths when danger threatens. The male and the female equally share this burden, though the female seems more willing.

Its almost impossible to believe that these three photos (see facing page and above) were taken within ten seconds of each other!!! The male actually has all of these baby fish in his buccal cavity . . . and I don't think he swallowed one of them.

The fry above were taken from the buccal cavity of a female *Melanochromis auratus* a few days after the eggs hatched. The lower photograph shows the fry a few days later, having absorbed their yolk and just about ready to look for their own food. Photos by Gerhard Marcuse.

This wonderful photograph by A.F. Orsini shows a female *Melanochromis auratus* releasing her young to feed. The young resemble miniature adult females, the males attaining their own pattern at maturity.

hardness, etc.), it can be generalized that eggs not fertilized within the first five minutes of being laid will never get fertilized. The reason for this is that the egg case begins to harden almost as soon as it hits the water. Once it becomes too hard the sperm are unable to penetrate the egg surface and thus the egg cannot be fertilized. This has important consequences in the acceptance or rejection of various theories of fertilization . . . for one must not be hasty in accepting the egg tassel theory (or the eggspot theory) . . . the physical properties giving rise to the theories might very well be recognition symbols . . . and this author believes they are nothing more than that!

Once the female (and in a few cases, the male) picks up the fertilized eggs, their incubation begins. Sometimes, if she happens to be an mbuna from Lake Malawi, she'll carry her eggs and young for three weeks, or even a month; other times, when the female might be a *Tropheus* from Tanganyika Lake, the poor female might be stuck with her eggs and fry for almost two

The female *Sarotherodon* accepting her fry.

months (56 days seems to be the record for a *Tropheus duboisi*). During this period the females do feed, regardless of what certain books say to the contrary. Some *Tilapia*, which brood for less than 3 weeks (19 days is about the average), however, can live without feeding, but they might feed while the fry are out of their mouths during the last week of their brooding period.

It has been very difficult to raise mouthbrooder eggs without a parent. The main reason for this is that the eggs are so heavy that the development within the egg is in a small area, the balance of the egg being utilized for food storage. If the eggs are not tumbled about and "chewed" during their storage in the mouth-brooder's buccal cavity, the yolk settles in the bottom of the egg, disturbing the development of the germinal disc and killing the developing embryo. A theoretical substitute for the mouth-brooder's cavity might be a 2 inch-diameter plastic tube through which air is bubbled to gently agitate the eggs on a continuous basis.

6
Breeding African Cichlids in the Aquarium

It is obvious that large areas in which huge nests can be built is practically impossible for the average home aquarium, yet so adaptable are the *Tilapia* and related genera of African fishes, including *Haplochromis*, that spawning them in aquaria is possible. The ability of the author to generalize about a "perfect spawning" aquarium is necessarily limited. It would be much safer to research in the various books on breeding aquarium fishes, or in hobbyist magazines where individual species are discussed, and attempt to lay out an aquarium suitable to fulfill the needs of the fish in question.

This is a typical rock outcrop in Lake Malawi. The rocks continue under the water in about the same configuration. This would be the ideal setup model for an aquarium, except in miniature of course.

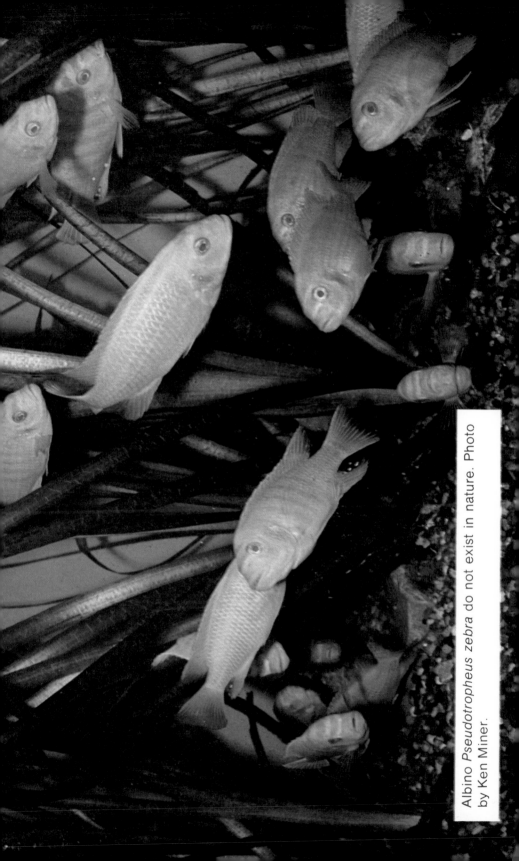

Albino *Pseudotropheus zebra* do not exist in nature. Photo by Ken Miner.

Haplochromis ornatus is found among the rocks of Lake Malawi. It is reported to develop small lobes on the lips, but not as prominent as those of *H. euchilus.* Photo by Aaron Norman.

The name of this fish in the hobby is *Haplochromis formosus* but it appears to look more like a species of mbuna than of *Haplochromis.* Photo by Aaron Norman.

For those fishes which build a sand nest, it would be advisable to have an aquarium with 4 inches or more of coarse sand on the bottom of the tank. A few rocks and submerged logs would probably be helpful, as would a large plant growing from a fairly heavy flowerpot. Needless to say, the larger the aquarium, the better. Certainly the aquarium should be at least 6 times as long and 4 times as wide as the length of the fish.

For mbunas and other rock dwellers, it would be advisable to have as many rocks and hiding places as possible, again with a deep base of coarse gravel. The mbunas will probably dig a pit under a rock and proceed with their spawning ritual as secretly as possible.

For the African cichlids which lay their eggs out in the open, or some of the 'Pelmatochromis' species of the Congo River system, large flat rocks would be advantageous.

A typical rocky bottom in Lake Malawi. The depth is about 35 feet.

A sandy, grassy habitat in Lake Malawi. Find the fish!

The majority of African cichlids are territorial. They stoutly defend their own territories even in their native habitat. Of course the territorial boundaries are basically imaginary, but let a newcomer to the aquarium dive into another fish's sanctuary and there likely will be serious trouble. For this reason, large aquaria are necessary, and crowding must be kept to a minimum. The only safe technique for introducing fishes to an already established aquarium in which there are many long-time residents is to move all the rocks and hiding places into new positions so all can have an equal chance to re-establish their territories.

Most African cichlids fight and bite each other, especially when males become breeding-conscious. You must watch your fishes closely and remove those fishes which seem to be getting the abuse. Once a fish becomes a loser, its demise cannot be far away, for fish lore is absolutely correct in its stress on "survival of the fittest." Most wise pet shop owners keep their African cichlids in tanks in which they have no place to hide. This allows for a better display of the fishes offered for sale and prevents territorialization. Unfortunately this type of accommodation

Telmatochromis vittatus from Lake Tanganyika differs from *T. bifrenatus* by the shape of the head, and the position of the mouth and angle of the stripe before the eye. Photo by Pierre Brichard.

Astatoreochromis straeleni from Lake Tanganyika was previously placed in the large genus *Haplochromis.* Photo by Aaron Norman.

This is a new species of *Xenotilapia* from the northern part of Lake Tanganyika. Photo by Pierre Brichard.

Reganochromis calliurum lives on sandy bottoms in the deeper waters of Lake Tanganyika. This beautiful fish is rarely seen in the hobby. Photo by Pierre Brichard.

keeps the cichlids in their least favorable coloration, but at least they are relatively safe from sexual and territorial competition.

If it is possible, pairs of mbunas and rock dwellers should be isolated in tanks with dimensions of at least 12 × 12 × 30 inches, though the author has used aquaria of 100 gallons in which six spawning pairs successfully found their own territories and were able to raise half a dozen babies on a fairly regular basis.

In outdoor pools in Florida, mbunas and Tanganyikan rock dwellers did very well. For one thing they rid the pool of tadpoles and crawfish. How they did this the author was unable to ascertain, but in pool after pool the tadpoles and crayfish gradually disappeared. A close examination of the pools, however, indicated that the mbunas, not having rocks, dug very deep caves, perhaps two feet deep, into the sides of the mud/clay banks. They successfully spawned and raised small quantities of fry, but as soon as the water temperature in the pools dropped below 68°, the mbunas had problems and gradually died. Perhaps they became the victims of snakes or water turtles as their metabolism slowed down?

Thirty feet depth in Lake Tanganyika. Lots of rocks, murky water and not much light or algae.

7
Diseases of
African Cichlids

African cichlids are relatively hardy fishes, as are most cichlids. They are susceptible to almost all the diseases of aquarium fishes, including but not limited to white spot disease (ichthyophthiriasis), slime bacterial infections which aquarists refer to as mouth fungus or tail or fin rot, and some fairly sophisticated diseases related to whirling disease (*Myxosoma*). In the thousands of mbuna that I observed and collected, almost every fish, most especially the smaller ones, were parasitized by the larval stages of several digenetic trematodes. It seems the metacercarial stage, one of the early stages in the development of the parasite, bores its way into the skin of the fish and forms a black cyst. In light-colored fishes the cysts are very obvious, while in darker fishes they are hardly noticeable. The cysts do not seem to aggravate the fishes; in tests the author made, the parasites required an intermediate host in order to reinfect other fishes in the same aquarium. It is quite possible that the fish itself is only one vector in the life history of the parasite, and in order for the encysted parasite to progress to the next stage in its life it must pass through the digestive tract of a fish-eating bird (of which there is no scarcity in the great lakes of Africa).

As a general rule, all African cichlids collected in their native ranges have black cysts and torn fins, but they quickly recover their full finnage if kept in situations which are non-competitive, usually within a week. The black cysts sometimes eventually disappear, as the cysts may well be expelled from the fish the way any foreign imbedment would be dislodged by the natural forces in most vertebrate animals. Thus African fishes with black spots are not to be considered as "diseased" though they certainly do harbor parasites.

White spots, bloody ulcers or open wounds are quite another story. These signs can only mean problems, and the most immediate attention should be paid to clearing up the condition as quickly as possible. There are many books on the diseases of fishes and it is almost unthinkable that any aquarist wouldn't have a few fish disease books in his library . . . they are probably the best investment one can make as far as the aquarium hobby is concerned.

A new species of *Pseudotropheus* from Lake Malawi. The new species in this book will be described in *Tropical Fish Hobbyist* magazine as soon as their characteristics have been thoroughly studied.

Haplochromis taeniolatus, head study of breeding male.
Note the parasites in the pectoral fin.

Lamprologus sp. (possibly *L. modestus*). Rather plain looking species of *Lamprologus* such as this one rarely are imported. Photo by Dr. Herbert R. Axelrod.

Limnochromis auritus frequents the deeper waters of Lake Tanganyika, around 40-60 meters. Photo by Dr. Herbert R. Axelrod.

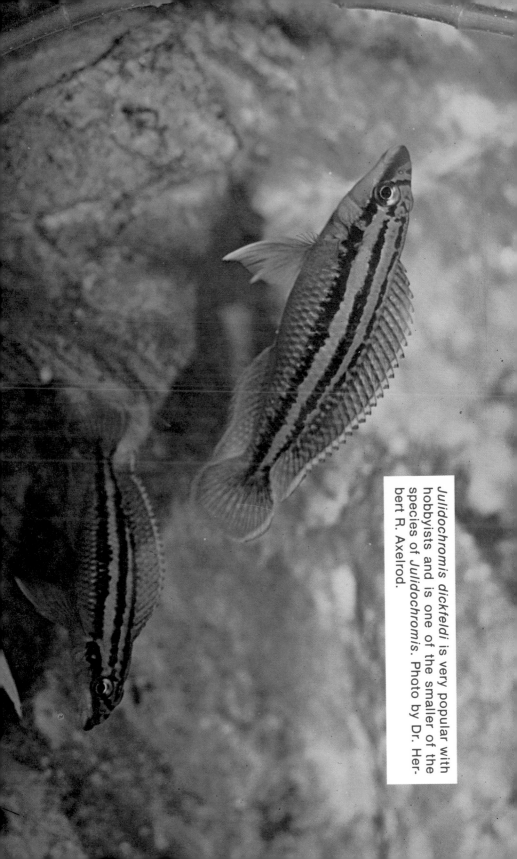

Julidochromis dickfeldi is very popular with hobbyists and is one of the smaller of the species of *Julidochromis*. Photo by Dr. Herbert R. Axelrod.

Pseudocrenilabrus philander(?) spawning in an aquarium. The female is picking up the eggs just as the male fertilizes them. Photo by Ruda Zukal.

The female *Pseudocrenilabrus philander*(?) with her buccal cavity bulging with eggs. Photo by Ruda Zukal.

Pseudotropheus lanisticola lives in an area where there are few rocks. It hides in empty shells of the genus *Lanistes.* It is quite surprising how a relatively large individual can squeeze itself into a relatively small shell. Only the tail of the fish can be seen in the shell below. Photo by Dr. Warren E. Burgess.

Pseudotropheus sp. ("eduardi"). The dorsal fin may or may not have a dark stripe in it like that of the anal fin. Some people consider the one with the stripe a separate species. Photo by A. Kochetov.

The red morph of *Pseudotropheus zebra.* Note the numerous small eye spots in the anal fin indicating this might be a male. Male red zebras command a premium price. Photo by Dr. Herbert R. Axelrod.

Haplochromis livingstonii.

Haplochromis decorus.

Haplochromis callipterus. The upper photo shows a close-up of the unpaired fins. Photos by Michael Oliver in Monkey Bay, Lake Malawi.

Labidochromis caeruleus is very delicately colored with pearl-like reflections often blue in color. Photo by G. Meola, African Fish Imports.

Labidochromis textilis has been successfully spawned in captivity as have most of the mbunas. Photo by G. Meola, African Fish Imports.

Pseudotropheus tropheops is often seen with orange blotching in the shoulder region. Photo by G. Meola, African Fish Imports.

Pseudotropheus sp. (center), possibly *P. tropheops,* hovering over some large rocks in its natural habitat in Lake Malawi. Photo by Dr. Warren E. Burgess.

Haplochromis stonemani.

Haplochromis macrostoma (?).

Haplochromis argyrosoma.

Haplochromis nitidus.

Pseudotropheus zebra may vary from what is called a pure white to heavily blotched. Above: White zebra morph. Below: Spotted zebra. Photos by G. Meola, African Fish Imports.

The spots have coalesced to larger blotches in the above *P. zebra* morph and much larger blotches covering a large part of the fish below. In all these photos note the eye spots in the dorsal, anal, caudal and even the pelvic fins. Photos by G. Meola, African Fish Imports.

Haplochromis subocularis. The eye has been discolored by the preservative (formalin) in which the fish was placed prematurely. Below is a closeup of the head (note the teeth) of the same fish.

Haplochromis anaphyrmus.

White morph of *Labeotropheus fuelleborni.* Some blotching can be seen. Photo by G. Meola, African Fish Imports.

Labeotropheus fuelleborni (blue fish) and species of *Pseudotropheus* feeding off the rock biocover in Lake Malawi. Photo by Dr. Warren E. Burgess.

One of the many colorful morphs of *Labeotropheus fuelleborni*. The red top and blue sides make this a popular fish. Photo by Dr. Herbert R. Axelrod.

The orange-sided *Labeotropheus fuelleborni*. The peculiar snout of the *Labeotropheus* species may eventually disappear with inbreeding. Photo by G. Meola, African Fish Imports.

Haplochromis pholidophorus.

Haplochromis nigritaeniatus.

Haplochromis annectens.

Haplochromis eucinostomus.

Haplochromis callipterus dines on snails in its native waters of Lake Malawi. Photo by Dr. Herbert R. Axelrod at the Berlin Aquarium.

Haplochromis sp. (possibly *H. strigatus*) from Lake Malawi. Interest in African cichlids seems to shift from mbuna to *Haplochromis* species and back again depending upon what new imports arrive. Photo by G. Meola, African Fish Imports.

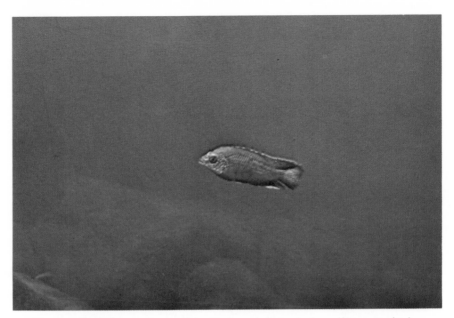

Haplochromis sp. (possibly *H. taeniolatus*). A solitary male individual above the rocks of Lake Malawi about 20 feet deep. Photo by Dr. Warren E. Burgess.

Most species keep rather close to the rock surfaces for feeding and for protection. Seen here are specimens of *Melanochromis* and *Labeotropheus*. Photo by Dr. Warren E. Burgess.

Haplochromis chrysonotus.

Haplochromis longimanus.

Haplochromis venustus, female above; male in photo below.

The gold blotch *Labeotropheus fuelleborni*. Species of *Labeotropheus* have about as many morphs as *Pseudotropheus zebra*. Photo by G. Meola, African Fish Imports.

Pseudotropheus species and a male *Labeotropheus fuelleborni* heading for deeper water and safety under the rocks. Photo by Dr. Warren E. Burgess at Lake Malawi.

One of the most prized morphs of the genus *Labeotropheus*, the red-top marmalade cat. Photo by G. Meola, African Fish Imports.

A group of mbuna including species of *Labeotropheus*, *Melanochromis* and *Pseudotropheus.* Photo by Dr. Warren E. Burgess.

Haplochromis kiwinge.

Haplochromis labridens.

Haplochromis taeniolatus.

Haplochromis jacksoni.

Aulonocara nyassae, the peacock blue or Malawi peacock in full breeding color. Photo by G. Meola, African Fish Imports.

The night *Aulonocara (Aulonocara nyassae)*, reaching a length of about 3-4", is the smallest of the peacock blue morphs. Photo by G. Meola, African Fish Imports.

The yellow "Aristochromis" is not a species of *Aristochromis* but a morph of *Aulonocara*. A better name would be yellow Aulonocara. Photo by G. Meola, African Fish Imports.

One of the newer imports is this as yet unidentified deep water *Haplochromis*. Photo by G. Meola, African Fish Imports.

Haplochromis atritaeniatus.

Haplochromis chrysonotus.

Haplochromis boadzulu.
Haplochromis virginalis.

8
Identifying African Cichlids

The classification of African cichlids, like the classification of all other fishes, is a highly specialized skill. The ichthyologists to whom fish classification is a specialty are known as taxonomists. They usually work in large public institutions and have developed fields of interest. It would be rare, for example, for an ichthyologist studying marine fishes also to undertake the study of a group of freshwater fishes, and it would be equally rare for a scientist studying cichlids to care to get involved in catfishes.

Lake Tanganyika. The fish in the foreground are *Lamprologus brichardi*; the single fish is *Julidochromis marlieri*.

African cichlids have a dozen or so working ichthyologists prying into their secrets. For the most part, the study of African cichlids has been centered in England, Belgium and Germany. Dr. Max Poll, the great Belgian ichthyologist, has spent a whole lifetime working on the fishes of the Congo, including a very thorough study of the fishes of Lake Tanganyika. Fryer, Eccles, Jackson and others have done extensive work on Lake Malawi. Essentially their work is concentrated in a few scientific books, mostly without any color photographs and without any photographs of living fishes. These scientists, for the most part, depend upon the characteristics of dead, preserved fishes upon which to make their determinations. They can, however, usually make a good guess about which fish is which from a good photograph, and should you have an identification problem, it would be best to send the photo to one of the recognized authorities in the field or check one of the more highly illustrated books.

Without a preserved specimen *positive* identification is almost impossible for any scientist.

For the purpose of this book, the author has selected a large variety of photographs to assist the beginner in identifying the most common fishes of Lakes Malawi and Tanganyika, with a few of the other popular African cichlids added for comparison. For a greater insight into understanding African cichlids there are two excellent texts which are readily available at every pet shop which specializes in fishes, or even at your local library. These books are:

The Cichlid Fishes of the Great Lakes of Africa by Dr. Geoffrey Fryer and T. D. Iles, and *Cichlids of the World* by Dr. Robert Goldstein. The Fryer and Iles book is a very scientific book, extremely well written, but poorly illustrated. The Goldstein effort is extremely well illustrated but not as scientifically detailed, though this by no means reduces its value for the non-scientist. Fryer and Iles is intended for scientists . . . Goldstein is intended for hobbyists. Both make excellent reading and are highly recommended.

*Hemitilapia oxyrhynchus,
with plant found in its range.*

9
Cichlids of Lake Malawi

The following list includes all the species of cichlids from Lake Malawi that are presently known. The study of these fishes is continuing and there will undoubtedly be new species being described from time to time.

Aristochromis christyi Trewavas
Aulonocara macrochir Trewavas
Aulonocara nyassae Regan
Aulonocara rostrata Trewavas
Chilotilapia rhoadesii (Boulenger)
Cleithrochromis bowleyi Eccles
Corematodus shiranus Boulenger
Corematodus taeniatus Trewavas
Cyathochromis obliquidens Trewavas
Cynotilapia afra (Gunther)
Cynotilapia axelrodi Burgess
Diplotaxodon argenteus Trewavas
Diplotaxodon ecclesi Burgess & Axelrod
Docimodus evelynae Eccles & Lewis
Docimodus johnstonii Boulenger
Genyochromis mento Trewavas
Gephyrochromis lawsi Fryer
Gephyrochromis moorii Boulenger
Haplochromis ahli Trewavas
Haplochromis anaphyrmus
  Burgess & Axelrod
Haplochromis annectens Regan
Haplochromis argyrosoma Regan
Haplochromis atritaeniatus Regan
Haplochromis auromarginatus (Boulenger)
Haplochromis balteatus Trewavas

Haplochromis boadzulu Iles
Haplochromis borleyi Iles
Haplochromis breviceps Regan
Haplochromis caeruleus Boulenger
Haplochromis callipterus (Gunther)
Haplochromis chrysogaster Trewavas
Haplochromis chrysonotus (Boulenger)
Haplochromis compressiceps (Boulenger)
Haplochromis cyaneus Trewavas
Haplochromis decorus Trewavas
Haplochromis dimidiatus (Gunther)
Haplochromis electra Burgess
Haplochromis epichorialis Trewavas
Haplochromis ericotaenia Regan
Haplochromis euchilus Trewavas
Haplochromis eucinostomus Regan
Haplochromis fenestratus Trewavas
Haplochromis festivus Trewavas
Haplochromis flavimanus Iles
Haplochromis formosus Trewavas
Haplochromis fuscotaeniatus Regan
Haplochromis gracilis Trewavas
Haplochromis guentheri Regan
Haplochromis hennydaviesae
  Burgess & Axelrod
Haplochromis heterodon Trewavas

165

Haplochromis heterotaenia Trewavas
Haplochromis holotaenia Trewavas
Haplochromis incola Trewavas
Haplochromis inornatus (Boulenger)
Haplochromis insignis Trewavas
Haplochromis intermedius (Gunther)
Haplochromis jacksoni Iles
Haplochromis johnstoni (Gunther)
Haplochromis kirkii (Gunther)
Haplochromis kiwinge Ahl
Haplochromis labidodon Trewavas
Haplochromis labifer Trewavas
Haplochromis labridens Trewavas
Haplochromis labrosus (Trewavas)
  (formerly *Melanochromis labrosus*)
Haplochromis lateristriga (Gunther)
Haplochromis lepturus Regan
Haplochromis leuciscus Regan
Haplochromis likomae Iles
Haplochromis linni Burgess & Axelrod
Haplochromis livingstoni (Gunther)
Haplochromis lobochilus Trewavas
Haplochromis longimanus Trewavas
Haplochromis macrostoma Regan
Haplochromis maculiceps Ahl
Haplochromis maculimanus Regan
Haplochromis marginatus Trewavas
Haplochromis melanonotus Regan
Haplochromis melanotaenia Regan
Haplochromis micrentodon Regan
Haplochromis microcephalus Trewavas
Haplochromis mloto Iles
Haplochromis modestus (Gunther)
Haplochromis mola Trewavas
Haplochromis mollis Trewavas
Haplochromis moorii (Boulenger)
Haplochromis nigritaeniatus Trewavas
Haplochromis nitidus Trewavas
Haplochromis nkatae Iles
Haplochromis nototaenia (Boulenger)
Haplochromis obtusus Trewavas
Haplochromis oculatus Trewavas

Haplochromis ornatus Regan
Haplochromis orthognathus Trewavas
Haplochromis ovatus Trewavas
Haplochromis pardalis Trewavas
Haplochromis phenochilus Trewavas
Haplochromis pholidophorus Trewavas
Haplochromis pictus Trewavas
Haplochromis placodon Regan
Haplochromis plagiotaenia Regan
Haplochromis pleurospilus Trewavas
Haplochromis pleurostigma Trewavas
Haplochromis pleurostigmoides Iles
Haplochromis pleurotaenia Boulenger
Haplochromis polyodon Trewavas
Haplochromis polystigma Regan
Haplochromis prostoma Trewavas
Haplochromis purpurans Trewavas
Haplochromis quadrimaculatus Regan
Haplochromis rhoadsii (Boulenger)
Haplochromis rostratus (Boulenger)
Haplochromis selenurus Regan
Haplochromis semipalatus Trewavas
Haplochromis serenus Trewavas
Haplochromis similis Regan
Haplochromis speciosus Trewavas
Haplochromis spectabilis Trewavas
Haplochromis sphaerodon Regan
Haplochromis spilonotus Trewavas
Haplochromis spilopterus Trewavas
Haplochromis spilorhynchus Regan
Haplochromis spilostichus Trewavas
Haplochromis stonemani Burgess &
  Axelrod
Haplochromis strigatus Regan
Haplochromis subocularis (Gunther)
Haplochromis taeniolatus Trewavas
Haplochromis tetraspilus Trewavas
Haplochromis tetrastigma Gunther
Haplochromis triaenodon Trewavas
Haplochromis trimaculatus Iles
Haplochromis urotaenia Regan
Haplochromis venustus Boulenger

Haplochromis virgatus Trewavas
Haplochromis virginalis Iles
Haplochromis woodi Regan
Hemitilapia oxyrhynchus (Boulenger)
Iodotropheus sprengerae Oliver &
  Loiselle
Labeotropheus fuelleborni Ahl
Labeotropheus trewavasae Fryer
Labidochromis caeruleus Fryer
Labidochromis fryeri Oliver
Labidochromis mathothoi Burgess &
  Axelrod
Labidochromis textilus Oliver
Labidochromis vellicans Trewavas
Lethrinops alba Regan
Lethrinops alta Trewavas
Lethrinops argentea Ahl
Lethrinops aurita (Regan)
Lethrinops brevis (Boulenger)
Lethrinops christyi Trewavas
Lethrinops cyrtonotus Trewavas
Lethrinops furcicauda Trewavas
Lethrinops furcifer Trewavas
Lethrinops gossei Burgess & Axelrod
Lethrinops intermedia Trewavas
Lethrinops laticeps Trewavas
Lethrinops leptodon Regan
Lethrinops lethrinus (Gunther)
Lethrinops liturus Trewavas
Lethrinops longimanus Trewavas
Lethrinops longipinnis Eccles & Lewis
Lethrinops lunaris Trewavas
Lethrinops macracanthus Trewavas
Lethrinops micrentodon Eccles & Lewis
Lethrinops microdon Eccles & Lewis
Lethrinops microstoma Trewavas
Lethrinops oculata Trewavas
Lethrinops parvidens Trewavas
Lethrinops polli Burgess & Axelrod
Lethrinops praeorbitalis (Regan)
Lethrinops stridei Eccles & Lewis
Lethrinops trilineata Trewavas

Lethrinops variabilis Trewavas
Lichnochromis acuticeps Trewavas
Melanochromis auratus (Boulenger)
  (formerly *Pseudotropheus auratus*)
Melanochromis brevis Trewavas
Melanochromis exasperatus Burgess
Melanochromis johanni (Eccles)
  (formerly *Pseudotropheus johanni*)
Melanochromis melanopterus Trewavas
Melanochromis parallelus Burgess &
  Axelrod
Melanochromis perspicax Trewavas
Melanochromis simulans Eccles
Melanochromis vermivorous Trewavas
Petrotilapia tridentiger Trewavas
Pseudocrenilabrus philander (Weber)
Pseudotropheus aurora Burgess
Pseudotropheus elegans Trewavas
Pseudotropheus elongatus Fryer
Pseudotropheus fainzilberi Staeck
Pseudotropheus fuscoides Fryer
Pseudotropheus fuscus Trewavas
Pseudotropheus lanisticola Burgess
Pseudotropheus livingstonii (Boulenger)
Pseudotropheus lombardoi Burgess
Pseudotropheus lucerna Trewavas
Pseudotropheus macrophthalmus Ahl
Pseudotropheus microstoma Trewavas
Pseudotropheus minutus Fryer
Pseudotropheus novemfasciatus Regan
Pseudotropheus tropheops tropheops Regan
Pseudotropheus tropheops gracilior
  Trewavas
Pseudotropheus tursiops Burgess
Pseudotropheus williamsi (Gunther)
Pseudotropheus zebra (Boulenger)
Rhamphochromis brevis Trewavas
Rhamphochromis esox (Boulenger)
Rhamphochromis ferox Regan
Rhamphochromis leptosoma Regan
Rhamphochromis longiceps (Gunther)
Rhamphochromis lucius Ahl

Triglachromis otostigma, young male above; *Limnochromis auritus* below. Photos by Dr. Herbert R. Axelrod.

Rhamphochromis macrophthalmus Regan
Rhamphochromis woodi Regan
Sarotherodon karongae (Trewavas)
Sarotherodon lidole (Trewavas)
Sarotherodon saka (Lowe)
Sarotherodon shirana (Boulenger)
Sarotherodon squamipinnis (Gunther)

Serranochromis robustus (Gunther)
Tilapia rendalli (Boulenger)
Tilapia sparrmani A. Smith
Trematocranus auditor Trewavas
Trematocranus brevirostris Trewavas
Trematocranus microstoma Trewavas
Trematocranus peterdaviesi Burgess & Axelrod

*Additional species of *Haplochromis* will undoubtedly be described in the near future.

There are many other "names" for the Malawi cichlids in the literature but for one reason or another they cannot be considered valid. Many of them are trade names, that is names coined by exporters or importers for use in identification but not validly described. These names may or may not even be applied to the same fish and in some cases there is more than one trade name to a fish (commonly an American and a European name exist for the same species). Some of these are: *Labeotropheus* "pernostus"; *Labidochromis* "mariniatus", *L.* "chisamulae", *L.* "fleeti", *L.* ewarti", *L.* "samueli", *L.* "chipoka", *L.* "pearl of chisamula"; *Cynotilapia* "mbenji", *C.* "eduardi"; *Melanochromis* "likomae", *M.* "chipokae", *M.* "caelestris", *M.* "ornatus"; *Pseudotropheus* "daviesi", *P.* "newsi", *P.* "patricki", *P.* "pindani", *P.* "eduardi", *P.* "kingsizei", *P.* "dingani", *P.* "sestoni", *P.* "mossambicus", *P.* "trevori", *P.* "mumbo", *P.* "malombe", *P.* "chipoka", *P.* "dubiatus," *P.* "fenestroma", *P.* "garmidiatus", *P.* "marmoratus", *P.* "greberi", *P.* "lilancinius," *P.* "kennyi," *P.* "jacksoni", *P.* "kingsleyi", *Trematocranus* "fryeri", *T.* "squamipinnis", etc.

A number of species have been inadequately described and the type specimens are such that identification at this time is uncertain. These species names should be considered nomena inquirenda (more information is needed to definitely ascertain what the fish really is). These are: *Labidochromis freibergi*, *L. joanjohnsonae*, *Melanochromis chipokae*, *M. interruptus*, *M. loriae*, *Microchromis zebroides*, *Pseudotropheus modestus*, *P. socolofi*, and *Trematocranus jacobfreibergi*.

Finally, a number of manuscript names or proposed names may turn up from time to time. These can not be listed here pending their description.

10
Cichlids of Lake Tanganyika

The following list includes all the species of cichlids from Lake Tanganyika that are presently known. Since the time of Prof. Max Poll's comprehensive treatment of the lake fishes in 1956, a number of taxonomic changes have been made and more than a dozen new species have been discovered. These have been added to Poll's basic list along with indications of what new species are being studied.

For a more comprehensive study of the fishes of Lake Tanganyika see Pierre Brichard's book *The Fishes of Lake Tanganyika*.

Asprotilapia leptura Blgr.
Astatoreochromis straeleni (Poll)
  (formerly *Haplochromis straeleni*)
Aulonocranus dewindti (Blgr.)
Bathybates fasciatus Blgr.
Bathybates ferox Blgr.
Bathybates graueri Stdr.
Bathybates horni Stdr.
Bathybates leo Poll
Bathybates minor Blgr.
Bathybates vittatus Blgr.
Boulengerochromis microlepis (Blgr.)
Callochromis macrops macrops (Blgr.)
Callochromis macrops melanostigma (Blgr.)
Callochromis pleurospilus (Blgr.)
Cardiopharynx schoutedeni Poll
Chalinochromis brichardi Poll

Cunningtonia longiventralis Blgr.
Cyathopharynx furcifer (Blgr.)
Cyphotilapia frontosa (Blgr.)
Cyprichromis leptosoma (Blgr.)
Cyprichromis microlepidotus (Poll)
Cyprichromis nigripinnis (Blgr.)
Ectodus descampsi (Blgr.)
Eretmodus cyanostictus Blgr.
Grammatotria lemairei Blgr.
Haplochromis benthicola Matthes
Haplochromis burtoni (Gunther)
Haplochromis horei (Gunther)
Haplochromis pfefferi Blgr.
  (formerly *Limnochromis pfefferi*)
Haplochromis stappersi Poll
Haplochromis vanderhorsti Greenwood
Haplotaxodon microlepis Blgr.
Haplotaxodon tricoti Poll

Hemibates stenosoma (Blgr.)
* Julidochromis dickfeldi Staeck
Julidochromis marlieri Poll
Julidochromis ornatus Blgr.
Julidochromis regani Poll
Julidochromis transcriptus Matthes
* Lamprologus attenuatus Stdr.
Lamprologus brevis Blgr.
Lamprologus brichardi Poll
Lamprologus callipterus Blgr.
Lamprologus calvus Poll
Lamprologus caudopunctatus Poll
Lamprologus christyi Trew. & Poll
Lamprologus compressiceps Blgr.
Lamprologus cunningtoni Blgr.
Lamprologus elongatus Blgr.
Lamprologus fasciatus Blgr.
Lamprologus furcifer Blgr.
Lamprologus hecqui Blgr.
Lamprologus kambaensis Staeck
Lamprologus kendalli Poll
Lamprologus kungweensis Poll
Lamprologus leleupi leleupi Poll
Lamprologus leleupi melas Matthes
Lamprologus leloupi Poll
Lamprologus lemairei Blgr.
Lamprologus meeli Poll
Lamprologus modestus (Blgr.)
Lamprologus mondabu Blgr.
Lamprologus moorei Blgr.
Lamprologus multifasciatus Blgr.
Lamprologus mustax Poll
Lamprologus niger Poll
Lamprologus obscurus Poll
Lamprologus ocellatus Stdr.
Lamprologus ornatipinnis Poll
Lamprologus petricola Poll
Lamprologus pleuromaculatus
  Trew. & Poll
Lamprologus prochilus Bailey
  & Stewart
Lamprologus profundicola Poll

Lamprologus pulcher Poll
Lamprologus savoryi Poll
Lamprologus schreyeni Poll
Lamprologus sexfasciatus Trew. & Poll
Lamprologus signatus Poll
Lamprologus stappersi Pellegrin
Lamprologus tetracanthus Blgr.
Lamprologus toae Poll
Lamprologus tretocephalus Blgr.
Lamprologus wauthioni Poll
Lestradea perspicax perspicax Poll
Lestradea perspicax stappersi Poll
Limnochromis abeelei Poll
Limnochromis auritus (Blgr.)
Limnochromis bellcrossei (Poll)
Limnochromis christyi Trewavas
Limnochromis dhanisi Poll
Limnochromis permaxillaris David
Limnochromis staneri Poll
Limnotilapia dardennei (Blgr.)
Limnotilapia loocki Poll
Limnotilapia trematocephala (Blgr.)
Lobochilotes labiatus Blgr.
Ophthalmochromis nasutus Poll &
  Matthes
Ophthalmochromis ventralis ventralis
  (Blgr.)
Ophthalmochromis ventralis heterodontus
  Poll & Matthes
Ophthalmotilapia boops (Blgr.)
Orthochromis malagaraziensis (David)
Perissodus eccentricus Liem & Stewart
Perissodus elaviae (Poll)
  (formerly Plecodus elaviae)
Perissodus hecqui (Blgr.)
  (formerly Xenochromis hecqui)
Perissodus microlepis Blgr.
Perissodus multidentatus (Poll)
  (formerly Plecodus multidentatus)
Perissodus paradoxus (Blgr.)
  (formerly Plecodus paradoxus)
Perissodus straeleni (Poll)
  (formerly Plecodus straeleni)

171

Petrochromis famula Mat. & Trew.
Petrochromis fasciolatus Blgr.
Petrochromis orthognathus Matthes
Petrochromis polyodon Blgr.
Petrochromis trewavasae Poll
Pseudocrenilabrus philander (Weber)
Reganochromis calliurus (Blgr.)
  (formerly Leptochromis calliurus)
Reganochromis centropomoides
  (Bailey & Stewart)
Reganochromis sp.
Sarotherodon karomo (Poll)
  (formerly Tilapia karomo)
Sarotherodon nilotica (Linne)
  (formerly Tilapia nilotica)
Sarotherodon tanganicae (Gunther)
  (formerly Tilapia tanganicae).
* Simochromis babaulti Pellegrin
Simochromis curvifrons Poll
Simochromis diagramma (Gunther)
Simochromis margaretae G. Axelrod
  & Harrison
Simochromis marginatus Poll
Simochromis pleurospilus Nelissen
Spathodus erythrodon Blgr.
Spathodus marlieri Poll
Tanganicodus irsacae Poll
Telmatochromis bifrenatus Myers
Telmatochromis burgeoni Poll
Telmatochromis caninus Poll
Telmatochromis temporalis Blgr.

Telmatochromis vittatus Blgr.
Tilapia rendalli Dumeril
  (formerly Tilapia melanopleura)
Trematocara caparti Poll
Trematocara kufferathi Poll
Trematocara macrostoma Poll
Trematocara marginatum Blgr.
Trematocara nigrifrons Blgr.
Trematocara stigmaticum Poll
Trematocara unimaculatum Blgr.
Trematocara variabile Poll
Triglachromis otostigma (Regan)
*Tropheus annectens Blgr.
Tropheus brichardi Nelissen & Thys
Tropheus duboisi Marlier
Tropheus moorei moorei Blgr.
Tropheus moorei kasabae Nelissen
Tropheus polli G. Axelrod.
Tylochromis polylepis (Blgr.)
Xenotilapia boulengeri (Poll)
Xenotilapia caudafasciata Poll
Xenotilapia longispinnis longispinnis Poll
Xenotilapia longispinnis burtoni Poll
Xenotilapia melanogenys (Blgr.)
Xenotilapia nigrolabiata Poll
Xenotilapia ochrogenys ochrogenys (Blgr.)
Xenotilapia ochrogenys bathyphilus Poll
Xenotilapia ornatipinnis Blgr.
Xenotilapia sima Blgr.
Xenotilapia spilopterus Poll & Stewart
Xenotilapia tenuidentata Poll

*There is a possibility of new species in the genera Lamprologus,
Julidochromis, Tropheus and Simochromis.

172

Diplotaxodon ecclesi.

Ophthalmochromis ventralis from Lake Tanganyika.

Haplochromis auromarginatus.

Haplochromis chrysonotus.

Haplochromis obtusus.

Haplochromis spilonotus.

Chilotilapia rhoadesii male in normal dress.

Chilotilapia rhoadesii male in breeding color.

Head study of *Chilotilapia rhoadesii.* The indentation on the upper lip is not normal.

Haplochromis fuscotaeniatus. This fish just died of suffocation by being kept in a small container for too long a period of time.

Haplochromis labridens.

Haplochromis polystigma, male, in breeding color.

Haplochromis taeniolatus, female.

Lethrinops gossei, female.

Lethrinops aurita.

Lethrinops parvidens.

Lethrinops polli.

Lethrinops furcicauda. Below, a closeup of the anal fin.

Lethrinops furcicauda, head study. Note the fine teeth. This dentition helps them dig out the chironomid larvae on sandy beaches. It has the long, pointed face common to most dirt-eaters (similar to the South American genus *Geophagus*).

Lethrinops christyi was once considered rare. The author collected dozens of them. The fish above is a breeding male; below is a closeup of the head. On the facing page is a detail of the anal fin and the egg spots.

Lethrinops lethrinus.

Pseudotropheus, a new species to be described in a future issue of *Tropical Fish Hobbyist* magazine.

Labidochromis fryeri from Maleri Island, Lake Malawi.
Trematocranus peterdaviesi.

Pseudotropheus elegans, female above; detail of unpaired fins below.

Pseudotropheus elegans male in breeding color.

Haplochromis modestus. Photo of a dead fish by Michael Oliver.

Melanochromis auratus, male dominant color.

A male *Melanochromis melanopterus* photographed in the lobby of the Monkey Bay Hotel on Monkey Bay, Malawi.

Pseudotropheus elongatus, male above, female below.

The above color morph of *Labeotropheus trewavasae* is very rare. Both fishes (above and below) appear to be females of the same species. The one below is in the familiar OB color pattern.

The overhanging snout is characteristic of species of the genus *Labeotropheus.* Here, in *Labeotropheus trewavasae,* the normal colored male is above, and the lower fish, a female, is of the peppered or mottled variety. Lake Malawi. Photo by Dr. Herbert R. Axelrod.

An atypical strain of *Labeotropheus trewavasae.* Probably not all of the different color varieties of this species have been described yet. Lake Malawi. Photo by Dr. Herbert R. Axelrod.

Labeotropheus fuelleborni has been successfully bred in home aquaria and is one of the favorites from Lake Malawi. In this pair the male is the upper fish. Photo by Stanley Lieberman.

The female *Labeotropheus trewavasae* carries the eggs. Here the "throat" is distended with her most recent brood. Lake Malawi. Photo by H. Hansen, Aquarium Berlin.

A male *Pseudotropheus microstoma* from Lake Malawi. Photo by Dr. R.J. Goldstein.

The female *Pseudotropheus microstoma* does not differ greatly from the male. Lake Malawi. Photo by Dr. R.J. Goldstein.

This *Pseudotropheus tropheops* male is much more brightly colored than the one on page 46. Lake Malawi. Photo by Dr. Herbert R. Axelrod.

Female (above) and male (below) *Melanochromis* cf. *johanni*, commonly called "ornatus" in the trade. Likoma Island, Lake Malawi.

Pseudotropheus elongatus, male from Lake Malawi. Photo by Karl Knaack.

A male (above) and what appears to be a female (below) *Cynotilapia afra*. These were captured in Lake Malawi near Likoma Island. Photo by Dr. Herbert R. Axelrod.

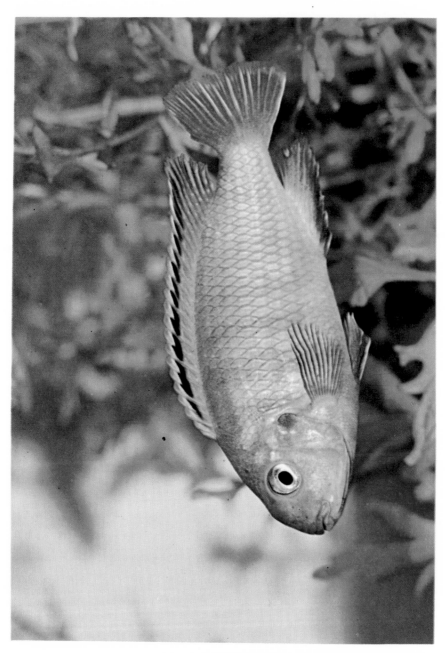

One of the plainer colored *Pseudotropheus tropheops* from Lake Malawi. Similar dark patterns of the fins are present in other species of African Lake cichlids. Photo by Dr. Herbert R. Axelrod.

Two female *Melanochromis* cf. *johanni*, the males of which appear on nearby pages. Lake Malawi near Likoma Island.

Pseudotropheus tropheops, male above, female below. These fish came from Lake Malawi near Likoma Island. Photo by Dr. Herbert R. Axelrod.

A *Pseudotropheus elongatus* male in its dark phase is just as colorful as *P. zebra*. But notice the elongate, or slender, body. Lake Malawi. Photo by D. Terver, Nancy Aquarium, France.

The fishes above and below and on pages 198 and 201 may be color morphs of *Melanochromis johanni.* They differ in proportions from specimens of *M. johanni* recently collected, but not from the specimens described by Eccles. Photos of specimens from near Likoma Island, Lake Malawi.

The color changes that the lake cichlids undergo are a source of confusion. It is difficult to believe that both these fish (above and below) are the same species, *Melanochromis vermivorus*. Lake Malawi. Photos by Hilmar Hansen, Aquarium Berlin.

The female *Melanochromis vermivorus* has a pattern like that of the male, but the colors are different as can be seen in this photo. Although this species has been bred in home aquaria, such reports are few and far between. Photo by G. Marcuse.

Probably one of the more confused species is this *Iodotropheus sprengerae,* commonly known as the rust or lavender cichlid. It had been confused with *Petrotilapia tridentiger,* which apparently is a different species altogether. Photo by Dr. R.J. Goldstein.

This species has been identified as both *Melanochromis brevis* and *Pseudotropheus lucerna.* The former name would probably be a better guess. Photo by Aaron Norman.

This yellow variety of *Pseudotropheus tropheops* shows some barring which can be compared with the specimen of reverse coloration on page 46. Photo by H. Hansen, Aquarium Berlin.

Pseudotropheus tropheops from Lake Malawi. This is probably another of the subspecies commonly attributed to the *P. tropheops* complex. Photo by Klaus Paysan.

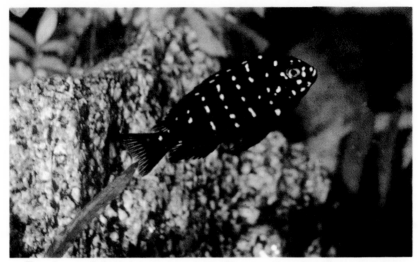

Tropheus duboisi, in contrast to *T. moorii,* is found in deeper water, and therefore does not appear in the trade very often. Lake Tanganyika. Juvenile photographed by Peter Chlupaty.

Tilapia sparrmanii has been found in the waters near Lake Malawi but as yet has not been found in the lake itself. It is omnivorous, and is one of the few nesting species in an otherwise mouthbrooding genus. Photo by Dr. R.J. Goldstein.

One of the better known fishes from Lake Tanganyika is *Tropheus moorii.* It is found in shallower water than *T. duboisi* and usually in a rocky area. Photo by Dr. Herbert R. Axelrod.

Tropheus moorii, like many other lake cichlids, is a mouthbrooder. The eggs are reported to be among the largest in the family Cichlidae. Lake Tanganyika. Photo by Dr. Herbert R. Axelrod.

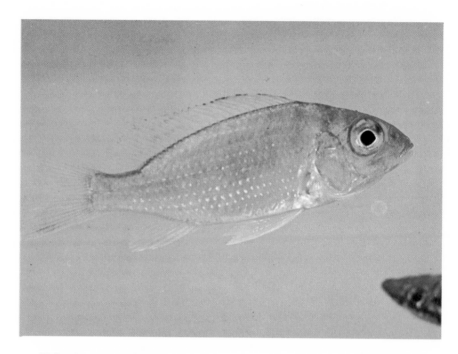

Tylochromis lateralis, young specimen above, adult below, from Lake Tanganyika. Species of this genus are thought to be maternal mouthbrooders; that is, the female cares for the eggs. Photo above by Dr. Herbert R. Axelrod, photo below by Hilmar Hansen, Aquarium Berlin.

A breeding male *Aulonocara macrochir* trawled from deep water in Lake Malawi. Photo by Michael K. Oliver.

Labidochromis fryeri from Mumbo Island, Lake Malawi. This is the typical coloration although the dark anal fin band is generally more blackish. Photo by H. Hansen, Aquarium Berlin.

This specimen of *Julidochromis* appears intermediate between *J. ornatus* and *J. transcriptus,* casting some doubt as to the validity of the latter species. Lake Tanganyika. Photo by Hilmar Hansen, Aquarium Berlin.

The complicated patterns in the fins and on the head make *Julidochromis marlieri* easy to recognize. It reaches a larger size than other species in the genus. Photo by Dr. R. J. Goldstein.

One of the more popular of African lake cichlids, *Lamprologus brichardi*. This fish used to go under the name *Lamprologus savoryi elongatus* but Dr. Max Poll has discovered that that name can no longer be used for this fish. The other *Lamprologus*, *L. savoryi savoryi*, will remain unchanged. Photo by H.J. Richter.

Lamprologus brichardi has been spawned in captivity as this and the following photos show. The male, to the left, is reported to have slightly longer finnage than the female. Photo by H.J. Richter.

The male approaches close to the female so that he can take position by her side as the eggs are laid, because he fertilizes them at the moment of extrusion. Photo by H.J. Richter.

The male and female undergo many different maneuvers during the actual spawning. Here the camera caught them in an unusual pose. Photo by H.J. Richter.

The site selected is usually a smooth rock such as those in the background. Photo by H.J. Richter.

The first eggs are visible on the gray rock in the lower right
hand corner of the photo. Photo by H.J. Richter.

Spawning continues, and more eggs will be deposited on the spawning site in due time. Photo by H.J. Richter.

The eggs are fairly large, amber colored, and adhere to the rock. Photo by H.J. Richter.

This *Lamprologus compressiceps* appears quite different from *L. brichardi* but are placed in the same genus. Photo by W. Hoppe.

Occasional imports include some of the other species of *Lamprologus,* such as *L. attenuatus.* It is a bottom nester from Lake Tanganyika. Photo by Dr. R.J. Goldstein.

Telmatochromis temporalis has often been confused with *Lamprologus petricola,* but *L. petricola* is a dark fish. The blue streak across the cheek appears to identify *temporalis.* Photo by Aaron Norman.

This specimen of *Haplochromis spilostichus* was trawled from 10-16 fathoms (60-100 feet) off Chembe village, Malawi. Photo by Michael K. Oliver.

A frequenter of the sandy shores of Lake Malawi is *Haplochromis strigatus.* Photo by Michael K. Oliver.

After examination of the specimens pictured, these fish turned out to be a new species and have been described as *Melanochromis exasperatus*. The upper fish is a young male and the lower photo is of a ripe female. Both came from Likoma Island, Lake Malawi. Photos by Dr. Herbert R. Axelrod.

A mixed group of cichlids from Lake Malawi. Upper fish is probably *Melanochromis perspicax*, center fish is a female *Labeotropheus fuelleborni*, and the lower fish is *Haplochromis livingstoni*. Photo by G. Marcuse.

Haplochromis venustus is a carnivorous cichlid from Lake Malawi which may be found in sandy areas and in grass beds. Photo by G. Marcuse.

A young *Haplochromis fuscotaeniatus* showing a color pattern similar to that of the adult (see p. 178). Photo by Warren E. Burgess.

The sulphur yellow nape is clearly visible on this *Haplochromis venustus*. Photo by Dr. Herbert R. Axelrod at the Berlin Aquarium.

One of the newer imports from Lake Malawi, the peacock blue cichlid. Specimens of this beautiful *Aulanocara nyassae* are hard to come by. Photo by Aaron Norman.

Hemitilapia oxyrhynchus is a browser among *Vallisneria* beds, scraping algae and insects from the leaves. Photo by Dr. Herbert R. Axelrod at the Berlin Aquarium.

Haplochromis sp. (possibly *H. jacksoni*). One must see this fish "in person" to appreciate its beauty. Photo by G. Marcuse.

One of the large-mouthed species, *Serranochromis robustus*. The dark lateral stripe is common to several species of Lake Malawi cichlids.

A species that often appears for sale is *Melanochromis perspicax* from Lake Malawi. This is a female. Photo by Warren E. Burgess.

The highly developed lips of this *Melanochromis labrosus* may be sensory in nature for the detection of food. Photo by Aaron Norman.

Males of many of the cichlids are often more colorful than the females. Although the upper individual of this pair of *Melanochromis brevis* was identified as a female and the lower one a male, I am inclined to think that the opposite is true. Photos by Warren E. Burgess.

Lobochilotes labiatus has also developed expanded or thickened lips, but apparently independently from *Melanochromis labrosus*. Photo by G. Marcuse.

←————

Melanochromis melanopterus is closely related to *M. vermivorus* and there has been confusion as to the identity of these two species. Photo by Dr. Herbert R. Axelrod.

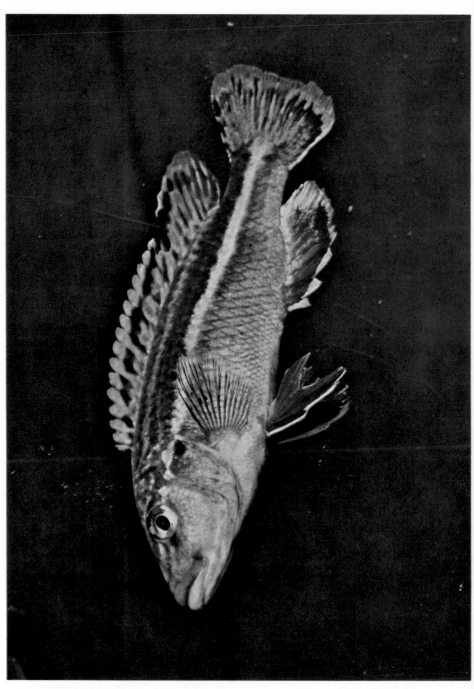

Melanochromis simulans(?) has a longer snout than *M. vermivorus*, but the color pattern is very similar (see pp. 204-5). Photo by G. Marcuse.

Not all of the African cichlids are big and heavy bodied. This slender *Limnochromis nigripinnis* is from Lake Tanganyika. Photo by Warren E. Burgess.

Telmatochromis vittatus is very close to and may be confused with *T. bifrenatus*. Individuals of the fish pictured here may be sold under either name. Photo by Warren E. Burgess.

A female (above) and male (below) *Melanochromis exas-peratus* (often incorrectly referred to as *Labidochromis joanjohnsonae*). This species is very popular with aquarists. Photo by Dr. Herbert R. Axelrod.

A new *Labidochromis* from Mumbo Island. Many Lake Malawi cichlids have this color pattern, but no other *Labidochromis*. Photo by Warren. E. Burgess.

An unidentified species of *Labidochromis* from Chisumulu Island, Lake Malawi. Photo by Warren E. Burgess.

The Likoma Island morph of a male *Melanochromis johanni* differs somewhat in pattern from the specimen shown on p. 48. Photo by Warren E. Burgess.

A female of the Likoma Island morph of *Melanochromis johanni.* No specific differences are apparent between this one and the female on p. 48. Photo by Warren E. Burgess.

The female *Pseudotropheus tropheops gracilior* shown here lacks the egg spots of the male. Photo by Warren E. Burgess.

The male *Pseudotropheus tropheops gracilior* is much more colorful than the female above. Photo by Warren E. Burgess.

Cynotilapia afra looks to all intents and purposes like *Pseudo-tropheus zebra*. In *Cynotilapia* the teeth are unicuspid, but in *Pseudotropheus* they are bicuspid.

A colorful *Cynotilapia* species from the Mozambique shores of Lake Malawi. Photo by Warren E. Burgess.

Lamprologus brichardi with some of the young swimming nearby. The small fish develop white edges to the caudal fin at an early age and look very much like the adults. Photo by H.J. Richter.

Spawns of African Rift Lake cichlids are generally small compared to the hundreds of eggs laid by other cichlids. One or two dozen fry are considered a successful spawn. Photo by H.J. Richter.

Another color variety of *Pseudotropheus zebra*. More morphs have been reported from Lake Malawi and may soon show up in the retail stores. Photo by G. Marcuse.

Pseudotropheus tropheops gracilior female from Likoma Island, Lake Malawi. Photo by Warren E. Burgess.

Trematocranus jacobfreibergi is a recent import from Lake Malawi. Photo by Dr. Herbert R. Axelrod.

Petrotilapia tridentiger is probably one of the largest of the mbunas. It also extends to a depth of over 200 feet and is likely limited in depth only by the lack of oxygen. Photo by Warren E. Burgess.

Labidochromis sp. from Chisumulu Island similar to that on p. 237 (top). Photo by Warren E. Burgess.

Labidochromis fryeri is less colorful than some of the other Lake Malawi cichlids. Photo by Warren E. Burgess.

The caudal fin pattern of *Pseudotropheus lanisticola* is very distinctive for an mbuna.

This laterally flattened species is *Haplochromis compressiceps*. It has received the common name Malawian eye-biter because of its habit of including the eyes of other fishes in its diet. The full-bodied view (above) and the close up of the head (below) give little indication of the extent of the compression of the body. Photos by Dr. Herbert R.Axelrod at the Berlin Aquarium.

The dark bars on this *Pseudotropheus* sp. have faded somewhat but this fish appears to be the one called "dingani" by aquarists. Photo by Hans J. Richter.

One of the *Pseudotropheus zebra*-like species which often goes under the trade name "dingani." Photo by Dr. Herbert R. Axelrod.

One of the newer imports is this tangerine *Pseudotropheus zebra*. Photo by G. Marcuse.

A very young *Pseudotropheus*, possibly *P. zebra*. The full color of the adult is not attained until later in its life. Photo by H.J. Richter.

A male *Pseudotropheus* sp. Note the long pelvic fins. Photo by Dr. Herbert R. Axelrod.

The female *Pseudotropheus* sp. incubates the eggs in her mouth. In the upper photo she is picking them up from the aquarium gravel where they were laid. In the lower photo she has finished, as indicated by her extended buccal area. This fish and the male opposite are often called "dingani."

Pseudotropheus tropheops variety from Likoma Island, Lake Malawi. Male. Photo by Warren E. Burgess.

A female of the *Pseudotropheus tropheops* variety from Likoma Island. Photo by Warren E. Burgess.

One of the color varieties of *Pseudotropheus tropheops*.
This color polymorphism causes considerable confusion in
African lake cichlid taxonomy. Photo by G. Marcuse.

African Rift Lake cichlids can be quite rough in an aquarium leaving some individuals in as sorry a state as this *Haplochromis longimanus*. Always provide plenty of cover to reduce losses. Photo by Dr. Herbert R. Axelrod.

Species of *Rhamphochromis* are predators, feeding on cich-lids of the "Utaka" group and *Engraulicypris sardella,* a cyprinid.

Lamprologus compressiceps received its name due to the highly compressed nature of its head. Photo courtesy Wardley Products Co.

A very colorful individual of *Iodotropheus sprengerae*. Only a few color morphs of this species have been imported. Photo by Stanislav Frank.

One of the more common color phases of *Iodotropheus sprengerae*. Notice it has the same pattern as the fish in the photo above. Photo by Jaroslav Elias.

A male (darker fish) and a female *Melanochromis parallelus*, which is currently known in the trade as the black-and-white auratus. Photo by Dr. Herbert R. Axelrod.

A group of male *Melanochromis* sp., probably *M. johanni*, with a red and a normal *Pseudotropheus zebra* nearby. Photo by Dr. Herbert R. Axelrod at the Berlin Aquarium.

A male (darker fish at back) and female (yellow fish) *Labeotropheus trewavasae*. The golden *trewavasae* are becoming very popular at this time. Photo by Dr. Herbert R. Axelrod.

A mottled **male** *Labeotropheus trewavasae*. This is the famous 'marmalade cat' and is apparently quite rare. Photo by Dr. Herbert R. Axelrod.

The normal male *Labeotropheus trewavasae* is quite an attractive fish and has become one of the most popular of the mbunas. Photo courtesy Wardley Products Co.

A normal mottled female *Labeotropheus trewavasae.* This one was found to be ripe with eggs. Note how closely it resembles the male marmalade cat opposite. Photo by Dr. Herbert R. Axelrod.

Labidochromis fryeri is readily recognizable by color and pattern as well as tooth characteristics. Its teeth, however, differ somewhat from the typical species of *Labidochromis*. Photo by Dr. Herbert R. Axelrod.

Although similar in pattern to *Labidochromis fryeri*, this fish (*Pseudotropheus* sp.) has different color and tooth characteristics. Photo by Dr. Herbert R. Axelrod.

This appears to be a male *Melanochromis exasperatus* in the dominant color phase. The orange striping is mostly hidden by the overall bluish color. Photo by H.J. Richter.

The female *Labidochromis textilis* is distinguishable in an aquarium from *Melanochromis exasperatus* females by the more numerous and more even horizontal stripes. Photo by Dr. Bruce J. Turner.

Labidochromis mathothoi, male above, female below. This is one of the less colorful species of *Labidochromis* as yet discovered and rarely, if ever, is imported.

Pseudotropheus minutus is shaped something like a *Labidochromis* but does not have the tooth structure of species of that genus.

Two male *Labidochromis vellicans*. The relatively shallow body, which is quite visible here, is one of the characteristics of the species.

Labidochromis sp., a brightly colored mbuna from Lake Malawi.

This bright blue mbuna goes under a number of names (*Pseudotropheus "eduardi," P. "pindani,"* and *P. socolofi*), none of which may be valid. This species does not exhibit sexual dimorphism. Photo by Dr. Herbert R. Axelrod.

The shape of the snout is distinctive in this pair of recently described mbuna, *Pseudotropheus tursiops*. The female is the top fish. Photo by Dr. Herbert R. Axelrod.

Pseudotropheus aurora is another recently described species that is recognizable by its large eye and bright yellow antero-ventral area. Photo by Dr. Herbert R. Axelrod.

The uncommon white male *Pseudotropheus zebra* still commands a relatively high price. Photo by Dr. Herbert R. Axelrod.

This female *Pseudotropheus zebra* morph had 19 ripe eggs in the right ovary. The color is unusual for zebras. Photo by Dr. Herbert R. Axelrod.

This mottled female *Pseudotropheus tropheops* has a background color similar to that of the female zebra on the opposite page. Photo by Dr. Herbert R. Axelrod.

A bright yellow morph of *Pseudotropheus tropheops* is becoming more common in the aquarium trade. Photo by Dr. Herbert R. Axelrod.

Petrotilapia tridentiger looks very much like a zebra in color pattern but can be recognized by looking at the mouth. Two males and a female (light colored fish) can be seen here. Photo by Dr. Robert Goldstein.

The teeth of *Petrotilapia tridentiger* are all tricuspid in contrast to species of the genus *Pseudotropheus* where the outer row is bicuspid. Photo by Dr. Herbert R. Axelrod.

A very beautiful color morph of *Cynotilapia afra*. Notice the resemblance of this species to *Pseudotropheus zebra* below. Photo by Dr. Herbert R. Axelrod.

Pseudotropheus zebra is now one of the mainstays of the African cichlid aquarium trade. It is often the first fish kept by those who want to start on the African lake cichlids. Photo by Dr. Herbert R. Axelrod.

A pair of *Telmatochromis caninus* guarding eggs laid under a flat rock. Photo by H.J. Richter.

Lamprologus tretocephalus is often confused with young *Cyphotilapia frontosa* although details of the banding are different.

Male *Pseudotropheus lombardoi* ("kennyi" or "lilancinius" in the trade) with its golden color, a reversal of the normal *Pseudotropheus* pattern. Photo by Ed Isaacs, Pet Gallery.

The female *Pseudotropheus lombardoi* is blue, also a reverse of the normal situation of male and female colors. Photo by Ed Isaacs of Pet Gallery.

Lamprologus elongatus from Lake Tanganyika. Photo by H. Scheuermann.

A spawning pair of *Lamprologus elongatus* with their most recent brood. Note the typical rocks-only African lake cichlid tank. Photo by H. Scheuermann.

Spathodus erythrodon. The characteristic blue spots are faint-
ly visible on the body and have turned dark on the head in this
frightened individual.

The shape of the body and head of goby-cichlids, like this
Eretmodus cyanostictus, indicates a bottom type existence.
Photo courtesy Wardley Products Co.

The great development
of the hump in
Haplochromis moorii
is shown in this close-up
photo. Photo by Michael
Oliver.

This young *Haplochromis moorii*, as shown here, is more
normal in appearance although the first indications of the
hump can be seen. Photo by Dr. Herbert R. Axelrod.

Red-top zebra, *Pseudotropheus zebra*. This is one of the many colorful morphs of *P. zebra* and is very popular in the hobby.

The horizontal stripes and barred caudal fin make *Julido-chromis regani* easily recognizable. Photo by Thierry Brichard.

Julidochromis transcriptus is very dark and has been called the masked *Julidochromis*. Photo by Thierry Brichard.

The second most popular species of *Julidochromis* (after *J. ornatus*) is *J. marlieri*. It is often available in aquarium stores dealing with African cichlids. Photo by Thierry Brichard.

There are several varieties of *Julidochromis* which are hard to place with any particular species. This one may be a pale form of *J. marlieri*. Photo by Thierry Brichard.

Several species of Lake Tanganyika cichlids are often confused. *Triglachromis otostigma* (formerly *Limnochromis otostigma*) was often mistaken for *Limnochromis auritus*. Photo by Homer Arment.

Limnochromis auritus resembles *T. otostigma* but has longitudinal light bluish stripes instead of diagonal ones. Photo by Dr. R.J. Goldstein.

This Lake Tanganyika fish is *Xenotilapia melanogenys*, one of the less common forms that rarely appear for sale. Photo by Aaron Norman.

Callochromis pleurospilus is one of the more colorful of the Lake Tanganyika fishes, but it has not gained very much in popularity. Photo by Dr. Herbert R. Axelrod.

The Malawian scale-eater, *Genyochromis mento*; females have this typical blotched color pattern. Photo by A. Ivanoff.

The male Malawian scale-eater. The common name is well deserved, and not many tank-mates are safe from its attacks. Photo by A. Ivanoff.

The Malawi peacock, *Aulonocara nyassae,* is one of the most popular Lake Malawi cichlids. The male shown here is from a population which lacks the orange shoulder area. Photo by Warren E. Burgess.

Females and young males of *Aulonocara nyassae* exhibit a striped pattern. Photo by Warren E. Burgess.

The large "egg" spots in the anal fin are clearly visible in *Haplochromis callipterus*. Photo by Dr. Herbert R. Axelrod.

One of the larger species of *Haplochromis* is *H. woodi*. Photo by Dr. Herbert R. Axelrod.

Some species of *Haplochromis* are more brightly colored than some of the mbunas. This one is *H. similis*. Photo by Dr. Herbert R. Axelrod.

Though obviously a male, this fish has none of the so-called "egg" spots in the anal fin. The orange spots in the dorsal fin, however, do resemble cichlid eggs in both size and color. Photo by Dr. Herbert R. Axelrod.

A young *Haplochromis rostratus*. The pattern of spots is characteristic, as is an extended snout which develops as the fish grows. Photo by Dr. Herbert R. Axelrod.

The large fleshy lips are well developed in this *Haplochromis euchilus* from Lake Malawi. Photo by Dr. Herbert R. Axelrod.

Haplochromis ericotaenia from Lake Malawi. Many of the *Haplochromis* species have this silvery color with blackish markings. Photo by Michael K. Oliver.

A young *Haplochromis fenestratus* in its fright color pattern. Photo by Dr. Robert J. Goldstein.

A close-up of the characteristic snout of *Haplochromis linni* from Lake Malawi. Photo by Dr. Herbert R. Axelrod.

A comparison photo showing two speckled species, *Haplochromis linni* (above) and *H. polystigma* (below). Photo by Dr. Herbert R. Axelrod.

Haplochromis johnstoni, one of the vertically barred cichlids from Lake Malawi. Photo by G. Meola, African Fish Imports.

Haplochromis livingstonii in a typical "yawning" pose. Photo by G. Meola, African Fish Imports.

Lamprologus tretocephalus. The dark bars extend into the dorsal fin here to a greater extent than in the other specimens pictured, possibly due to age. Photo by H. Scheuermann.

Lamprologus tretocephalus is often confused with *L. sexfasciatus*, but has only three bars below the dorsal fin in comparison with four for *sexfasciatus.* Photo by G. Meola, African Fish Imports.

A group of small *L. tretocephalus* in a basically rock-decorated African cichlid tank. Photo by G. Meola, African Fish Imports.

The young spotted form of *Tropheus duboisi* from Lake Tanganyika.

With age the spots of *Tropheus duboisi* disappear.

The typical *Tropheus moorii* male is dark with a band of color (red, yellow, white, etc.) across the body behind the pectoral fin.

Several new morphs of *Tropheus moorii* have appeared recently, including this striped form.

Chalinochromis brichardi morph in which the juvenile spotted pattern is retained in the adult stage. Photo by G. Meola, African Fish Imports.

The striped pattern of *Chalinochromis brichardi* looks quite similar to that of *Julidochromis dickfeldi.* Photo by G. Meola, African Fish Imports.

The markings of the head of *Chalinochromis brichardi* are quite distinctive. Note the extra stripe behind the eye (lacking in *Chalinochromis* sp.) and the lower jaw teeth.

Adult and near adult *Chalinochromis brichardi*. Even the last dorsal spot may eventually disappear.

Julidochromis regani. The fin pattern of this individual has all but disappeared.

Diplotaxodon argenteus has been captured at depths of 30-40 meters where it feeds on other fishes, mainly *Engraulocypris.*

The golden form of *Lamprologus leleupi.* This species should not be confused with *L. leloupi,* an entirely different fish.

Haplochromis fuscotaeniatus male from Lake Malawi in spawning coloration. Photo by G. Meola, African Fish Imports.

Lamprologus compressiceps of Lake Tanganyika. Note the proportionately large mouth.

Petrochromis polyodon, probably a female with shorter fins.

Closeup of the mouth and teeth of *Petrochromis polyodon.*
Note the similarity between the teeth of this species and
Petrotilapia tridentiger of Lake Malawi (p. 270).

Adult male *Petrochromis polyodon* with filaments on the unpaired and pelvic fins. Note also the "egg-spots" in the dorsal
and anal fins.

Haplochromis modestus male in breeding color. Compare this with the fish on p. 189. Photo by Warren E. Burgess.

Haplochromis sp. (possibly *H. woodi*). The position of the dark spots along the side and back is characteristic. Photo by Warren E. Burgess.

Above and below: Trematocranus sp. This fish has been sold under the trade name "Red-Top *Aristochromis*" even though there is no resemblance at all between *Trematocranus* and the true *Aristochromis*. Photos by G. Meola, African Fish Imports.

Haplochromis of the *modestus*-complex, dark male. Photo by Warren E. Burgess.

Non-dominant male *Haplochromis* of the *modestus*-complex, presumably the same species as the above. Photo by Warren E. Burgess.

Lethrinops sp. Still as yet unidentified and possibly a new species. Photo by Warren E. Burgess.

Haplochromis sp. Breeding male, possibly *H. mollis* or another diagonally striped *Haplochromis.* Photo by Warren E. Burgess.

Young male *Trematocranus jacobfreibergi* just starting to develop some of the coloring of the adult male. Photo by Warren E. Burgess.

Female *Trematocranus jacobfreibergi* are banded and not very colorful. Photo by Warren E. Burgess.

Adult male *Trematocranus jacobfreibergi* in dark breeding color. The stripes are barely discernible.

Adult male *Trematocranus jacobfreibergi* in a lighter color phase than the one above. Photo by G. Meola, African Fish Imports.

The juvenile *Pseudotropheus elegans* shown here is very similar to the adults shown on previous pages. Photo by Warren E. Burgess.

Cynotilapia afra, "eduardi" form with the striped dorsal. This fish was a ripe male. Photo by Warren E. Burgess.

Cynotilapia axelrodi female has less intense color than the male. This female was nearly ripe. Photo by Warren E. Burgess.

Cynotilapia axelrodi, male. The anal fin color might serve to distinguish the male from the female of this species. Photo by Warren E. Burgess.

Labidochromis vellicans was the first species of *Labidochromis* to be discovered and named. Photo by Warren E. Burgess.

Labidochromis fryeri diverges slightly from the basic *Labidochromis* stock by having weakly bicuspid teeth. Photo by Warren E. Burgess.

The true *Labidochromis caeruleus* has dark stripes in the dorsal and anal fins. Photo by Warren E. Burgess.

Another phase of *Labidochromis caeruleus* with less blue. Both this fish and the one above are males. Photo by Warren E. Burgess.

Above and below: Pseudotropheus (or *Labidochromis*) *minutus.* The above specimen has more bars and the specimen below has indications of a dorsal fin stripe, but both appear to be the same species. Photo above by Warren E. Burgess; photo below by G. Meola, African Fish Imports.

Above and below: Labidochromis sp. The male (above) is darker and generally more colorful than the female (below). Both of these fishes were ripe when captured. Photos by Warren E. Burgess.

A relatively new importation, the black-top fuelleborni. Many new varieties of *Labeotropheus fuelleborni* are still being discovered. Photo by Warren E. Burgess.

One of the popular varieties of *Labeotropheus fuelleborni* is the orange-sided fuelleborni shown here.

The very colorful OB or orange blotched *Labeotropheus fuelleborni* is almost always a female. Photo by Warren E. Burgess.

Occasionally an OB male *Labeotropheus fuelleborni* is found and can be recognized by the bluish tints on the body. It is called the marmalade cat just as the OB male of *L. trewavasae* is. Photo by G. Meola, African Fish Imports.

Pseudotropheus sp. This fish is called "jacksoni" in the trade. Photo by G. Meola, African Fish Imports.

Pseudotropheus sp. In addition to the names given on p. 266, this species is also commonly called "newsi" in the trade. Photo by G. Meola, African Fish Imports.

Pseudotropheus sp. This *P. zebra*-like species has a very unusual color and the teeth differ from those of the true *P. zebra*. Photo by Warren E. Burgess.

Pseudotropheus zebra, mottled variety. This seems to be a variation of the OB zebra female. Photo by Warren E. Burgess.

Pseudotropheus microstoma, dark phase. The steeply descending snout marks this as a member of the *P. tropheops* complex. Photo by Warren E. Burgess.

Pseudotropheus sp. No definite identification of this fish has yet been determined.

This is a photograph of the holotype of the shell-dwelling species *Pseudotropheus lanisticola*. Photo by Warren E. Burgess.

This large-lipped *Haplochromis* sp. (probably a breeding male *H. euchilus*) has affectionately been called the "Super VC-10" (after the jet plane) by Peter Davies. Photo by Warren E. Burgess.

Pseudotropheus sp. of the *P. elongatus*-complex. This species has been called various names in the trade, the most recent being "bentoni." Photo by Warren E. Burgess.

Pseudotropheus elongatus is a very slender bodied mbuna and can be easily identified. Photo by Warren E. Burgess.

Melanochromis vermivorus male in breeding color. Note the whitish dorsal fin. Photo by Warren E. Burgess.

Melanochromis parallelus male. The dorsal fin is dark in this species and the lateral stripes are bluish, here blending into the dark background of the fish. Photo by Warren E. Burgess.

Female *Melanochromis* "chipokae" (above) and male of the same species (below) showing the typical *Melanochromis* patterns, dark stripes on a light background in the female and light stripes on a dark background in the male. Photos by G. Meola, African Fish Imports.

Simochromis curvifrons. Photo by Glen Axelrod.

Simochromis marginatus. Photo by Glen Axelrod.

Cyathopharynx furcifer. Photo by Glen Axelrod.

Telmatochromis bifrenatus. Photo by Glen Axelrod.

Lobochilotes labiatus. Photo by Glen Axelrod.

Lobochilotes labiatus. Head photo by Glen Axelrod.

Tanganicodus irsacae. Photo by Glen Axelrod.

Tanganicodus irsacae. Color phase. Photo by Glen Axelrod.

Eretmodus cyanostictus. Photo by Glen Axelrod.

Spathodus erythrodon. Photo by Glen Axelrod.

Petrochromis polyodon. Photo by Glen S. Axelrod.
Petrochromis fasciolatus. Photo by Glen S. Axelrod.

Petrochromis sp. Photo by Glen Axelrod.

Petrochromis sp. Photo by Glen Axelrod.

Limnochromis leptosoma. Photo by Glen Axelrod.

Limnochromis leptosoma. Males and females. Photo by Glen Axelrod.

Julidochromis regani. Southern form. Photo by Glen Axelrod.

Ophthalmochromis ventralis. Photo by Glen Axelrod.

Haplochromis burtoni. Photo by Glen Axelrod.
Haplochromis burtoni. Fin patterns. Photo by Glen Axelrod.

Lamprologus tetracanthus. With young. Photo by Glen Axelrod.
Lamprologus tetracanthus. Photo by Glen Axelrod.

Haplochromis horei. Photo by Glen Axelrod.

Haplochromis horei. Female. Photo by Glen Axelrod.

Haplochromis horei. Head pattern. Photo by Glen Axelrod.

Lamprologus fasciatus. Photo by Glen Axelrod.

Tropheus moorii. Red form. Photo by Glen Axelrod.

Tropheus moorii. Red form from south. Photo by Glen Axelrod.

Tropheus moorii. Yellow-belly form. Photo by Glen Axelrod.

Tropheus moorii. Form from Kigoma. Photo by Glen Axelrod.

Tropheus moorii. Brown form. Photo by Glen Axelrod.
Tropheus moorii. Green form. Photo by Glen Axelrod.

Tropheus moorii. Yellow form. Photo by Glen Axelrod.
Tropheus moorii. Fry. Photo by Glen Axelrod.

Tropheus duboisi. Narrow olive band. Photo by Glen Axelrod.

Tropheus duboisi. Wide olive band. Photo by Glen Axelrod.

Tropheus duboisi. White band. Photo by Glen Axelrod.

Tropheus duboisi. White band. Photo by Glen Axelrod.

Lamprologus compressiceps. Red form. Photo by Glen Axelrod.

Lamprologus compressiceps. Red form. Photo by Glen Axelrod.

Lamprologus compressiceps. Yellow. Photo by Glen Axelrod.

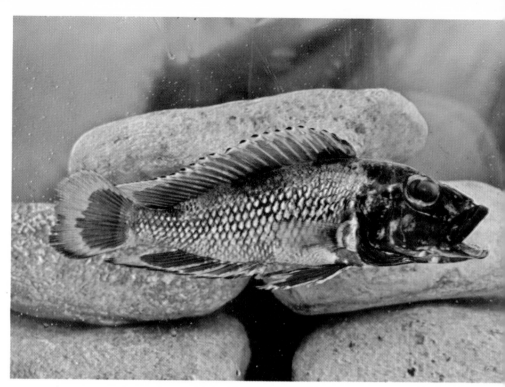

Lamprologus lemairei. Photo by Glen Axelrod.
Lamprologus furcifer. Photo by Glen Axelrod.

Lamprologus tretocephalus. With young. Photo by G. Axelrod.
Lamprologus tretocephalus. With young. Photo by Glen Axelrod.

Pseudotropheus sp. Photo by Glen Axelrod.

Pseudotropheus sp. Lake Malawi. Photo by Glen Axelrod.

Perissodus straeleni. Photo by Glen Axelrod.

Perissodus straeleni. Head pattern. Photo by Glen Axelrod.

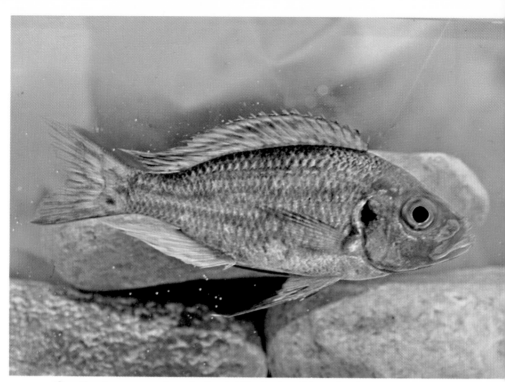

Cardiopharynx schoutedeni. Photo by Glen S. Axelrod.

Haplochromis sp. Photo by Glen S. Axelrod.

Sarotherodon tanganicae. Photo by Glen S. Axelrod.

Sarotherodon sp. Photo by Glen S. Axelrod.

Tropheus polli. Photo by Glen S. Axelrod.

Spathodus erythrodon. Photo by Glen S. Axelrod.

Haplochromis sp. Photo by Glen Axelrod.

Haplochromis sp. Photo by Glen Axelrod.

Aulonocranus dewindti. Photo by Glen Axelrod.

Xenotilapia longispinis longispinis. Photo by G. Axelrod.

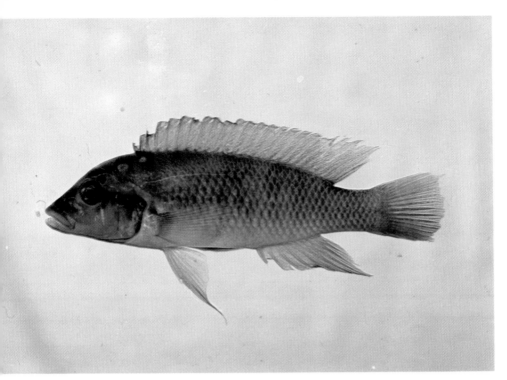

Lamprologus sp. Photo by Glen S. Axelrod.

Lamprologus toae. Photo by Glen S. Axelrod.

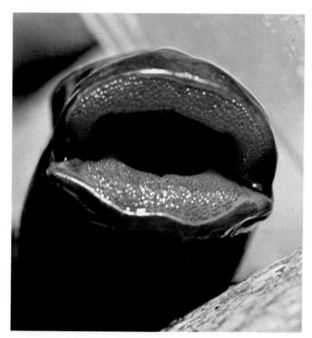

Petrochromis polyodon. Photo by Glen Axelrod.

Petrochromis polyodon. Photo by Glen Axelrod.

Labeotropheus fuelleborni. The male above has orange tips on his fins. The female, below, has the same color pattern as the normal color of *L. trewavasae* and they are frequently confused.

The top fish is a male *Labeotropheus trewavasae,* the lower fish is an OB female morph. Photos by Dr. D. Terver at the Nancy Aquarium.

Labeotropheus fuelleborni fry above and adult male below.
Photographs by Dr. D. Terver at the Nancy Aquarium.

Plecodus paradoxus.

Cyphotilapia frontosa.

Petrochromis polyodon.

Spathodus erythrodon.

Callochromis macrops melanostigma.

Haplochromis horei.

Callochromis pleurospilus, female above, male below.

Limnotilapia dardennei.

Perissodus microlepis.

Simochromis babaulti.

Simochromis diagramma.

Limnochromis auritus.

Xenotilapia sima.

Haplochromis pfefferi.

Xenotilapia boulengeri.

Lobochilotes labiatus, head study above; side view below.

Sarotherodon tanganicae, about 18 inches long, bought at the Bujumburu fish market. Somehow the fly landed while the photo was being taken.

Telmatochromis bifrenatus.

Telmatochromis caninus.

Head study of *Telmatochromis caninus*.

Lamprologus callipterus, female above, male below. The plants in all photographs in this book (except those taken in aquaria) are authentic and are found with the fishes in the same lake.

Lamprologus brichardi.

Lamprologus savoryi.

Lamprologus leleupi.

Lamprologus modestus.

Lamprologus tetracanthus.

Lamprologus modestus.

Lamprologus cunningtoni.

Lamprologus elongatus.

Haplochromis moorii from Lake Malawi is not closely related to *Cyphotilapia frontosa* of Lake Tanganyika, even though they are similar in general shape. Their living colors are quite distinct. This fish is *H. moorii.*

Telmatochromis caninus, closeup of the head. The line run-
ning from the bottom of the eye is usually much blacker.

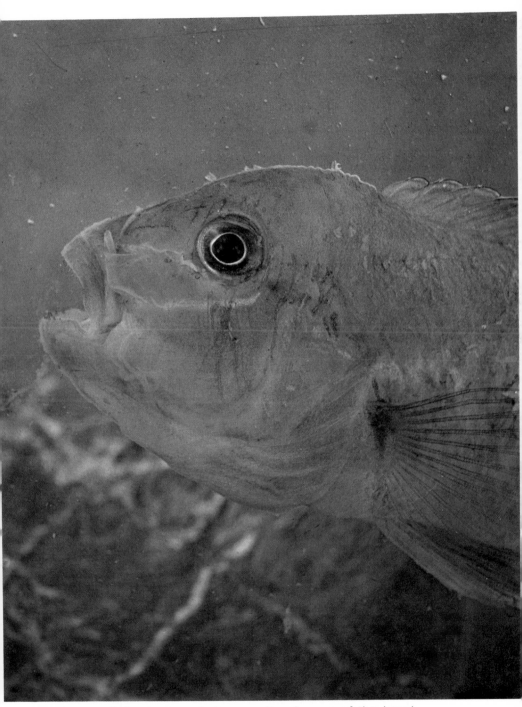

Telmatochromis temporalis, closeup of the head.

Haplochromis heterotaenia. Photo by Michael K. Oliver.

Haplochromis woodi. Photo by Michael K. Oliver.

Eretmodus cyanostictus.

Haplochromis epichorialis. Photo by Michael Oliver.

Haplochromis fenestratus male in almost complete breeding dress. Photo by Michael Oliver.

Haplochromis euchilus, female. Photo by Hilmar Hansen, Berlin Aquarium.

Haplochromis mloto, male above, female below. Note egg-spots on female's anal fin.

Haplochromis chrysonotus.

Haplochromis lepturus.

Limnochromis auritus, a close-up of the head of a breeding male. Photo by Dr. Herbert R. Axelrod.

Telmatochromis temporalis.

Cyphotilapia frontosa, just starting to get the lump on its forehead. Photo by Hilmar Hansen, Aquarium Berlin.

ILLUSTRATIONS INDEX

*The changing of *Pseudotropheus auratus* and *Pseudotropheus johanni* to *Melanochromis auratus* and *Melanochromis johanni* respectively was made too late to incorporate it into the previous editions of this book and therefore these species may still be captioned under the old names on some pages.